STUDY GUIDE

TO ACCOMPANY

HUMAN SEXUALITY

by Bryan Strong and Christine DeVault

Developed by

Bobbi Mitzenmacher
California State University, Long Beach

Barbara Werner Sayad
San Jose State University

Mayfield Publishing Company
Mountain View, California
London • Toronto

To Frank, Bryan, and Christine for the opportunity to do this study guide; to Sol Gordon, Jeanne Lindsey, and my students for being inspirations; to Joanne, Goldie, Cookie, Mike, Steve, Danny, Bill and Sandi for their friendship and encouragement; and to my husband Myron for his help and support in everything I do. — Bobbi Mitzenmacher

To my husband, Bob; to my children, Sarah, Elizabeth and Sam; and to the many students who have made this project meaningful to me. — Barbara Werner Sayad

International Standard Book Number 1-55934-341-9

Manufactured in the United States of America
10 9 8 7 6 5 4 3 2

Mayfield Publishing Company
1280 Villa Street
Mountain View, California 94041

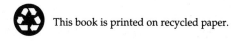

This book is printed on recycled paper.

To the Student

This study guide is designed to help you achieve two important goals in learning about human sexuality. First, it will make it easier for you to study, review, and comprehend the material you are learning from the textbook, *Human Sexuality,* by Bryan Strong and Christine DeVault. Although it is true that each of us already possesses some knowledge about human sexuality, you will be surprised by the amount of new information as well as the number of terms and ideas that will be presented in the class and the textbook. This study guide will increase your success in learning, retaining, and integrating the essential information.

Second, but of equal importance, this study guide will give you opportunities to think about human sexuality research and issues in terms of your own life. Sexuality is not just about sexual activity. It is a matter that affects one's biological, psychological, cultural, and ethical makeup. Unlike any other class you will take in college, the ideas you will be learning about, the objective information that is presented, and the applications that are possible have the potential to affect your future behavior and personal development. The Gender and Sexual Identity section (described in detail below) at the end of each chapter in Part II of this study guide is designed to help you with this exploration. Your comments and answers to these exercises should be honest and personal, so you may want to tear out those pages and keep them in a private place.

To help you focus on key concepts, each chapter of the study guide begins with a set of learning objectives. Before you read each chapter in the textbook, you may want to review the learning objectives for that chapter in this guide. Each chapter also includes a practice test of multiple choice, true/false, fill-in questions that test your knowledge of key terms, and short answer or essay questions. These practice tests are designed to help you assess how well you have mastered the core information in the chapter. You may wish to give special attention and additional review to any questions that you missed or feel uncertain about even if you did guess at the correct answer.

The next two sections of each chapter are included to make the information you are learning more personally meaningful. Observations and Reflections exercises provide out-of-class opportunities to relate information about sexuality to your personal experience or to an observation. For example, exercises may include conducting an interview, observing and recording people's behavior in a public setting, or watching a TV program or commercial to gain insight into what messages are being given about males and females, relationships, and sexual behavior. To help apply material to your own experience, exercises entitled Personal Involvement Assessment include exercises, assessments, and questions for analyzing how information in the chapter relates to your experience, behavior, and opinions.

The variety of activities suggested in each chapter allows you the freedom to choose those that you feel are meaningful and relevant to your life. Because a number of them are sensitive in nature, we urge you to use your good judgment when you interview others and in responding to the statements made by others.

One experiential exercise is worth special mention. In Part I of this study guide, you will find information about a Gender and Sexual Identity section at the end of each chapter. This section asks you to think about and reflect on your personal history of gender and sexual identity. Each section (marked by a rose) contains questions for you to answer and open-ended statements for you to complete. Completing this exercise will help you see where and how your sexual self originated and developed. In addition to the exercise, each of these sections has relevant statements from students that will help you see other points of view. This very personal and revealing exploration is likely to give you meaningful insights and growth beyond the expectations you had when you entered this course.

Each student comes to this class with a unique background. Some students have had negative experiences or feelings about sexuality. Others have had little or no direct sexual experience. Some students in every class have had positive experiences. No matter what our experiences are, we are all capable of learning and accepting others as well as ourselves. The more we observe and explore, the more likely we are to achieve positive gains. Our sexual behaviors can be a positive and constructive part of our lives, and we hope your efforts in completing these activities and exercises helps you become more comfortable with the subject of human sexuality and with your personal sexuality.

Contents

PART I

General Resources

GETTING TO KNOW YOUR TEXTBOOK: A SELF-GUIDED TOUR

Over the next few months, you'll be spending considerable time with your textbook. Along with lectures and discussions, the textbook will be one of your most important learning tools. We have given much thought to how the various elements of the textbook fit together. These different elements form a whole, whose aim is to further your understanding of human sexuality.

We have designed the questions below to provide you with a self-guided learning tour through the textbook. (Most examples will be taken from Chapter 1.) You will explore each element. When you have completed this tour, you will be able to use the textbook to its full advantage.

As you answer each question, write down your responses on a separate sheet of paper. Your responses should be very brief, usually not more than a sentence or two. Your instructor may want you to turn it in.

First, take a few minutes to browse through the textbook to get a feel for it. What is your first impression of the book?

Read the "Student Prologue." In the section entitled "The Authors' Perspective," we describe several themes in the textbook. Briefly list what the themes are.

Read through the table of contents. This gives you an overview of what the textbook will cover. What is the title of the chapter that looks most interesting to you?

Each chapter begins with a non-graded true/false preview quiz. The previews are designed to give you an idea of what you'll find in the chapter—and what you may already know or not know. They are for fun; they will not be graded. Take the preview quiz for Chapter 1. If you missed any questions, list their numbers.

Following the preview, each chapter has an outline that succinctly describes the structure of that chapter. Read the outline to get an idea of what the chapter will cover.

You'll find a chapter summary after the main body of text in each chapter. Before you read the chapter text, read the summary for Chapter 1. Reading the summary first will make reading the chapter easier.

Skim through the main text in Chapter 1.

After the chapter summary you'll find a list of key terms. These are important terms that you should know. They are printed in boldface when they first appear and are described in the text. In the key terms list, the terms are arranged in the order they appear in the chapter text. Within the main text of Chapter 1, find the first key term that appears on the list and define it.

Go to the glossary at the end of the textbook where all the key terms are defined. Find the same key term in the glossary. Now find a term in the glossary you don't know and define it here.

After the key terms list in the chapter, you'll find Suggestions for Further Readings. What is the title of the book that looks most interesting to you?

Each chapter has one or more Perspectives designed to go into a subject in greater depth or provide you with another way of looking at things. Read the Perspective in Chapter 1. Do you think there should be gender testing in sports? Why?

Many chapters have Self-Assessments that will help you evaluate your feelings, attitudes, or knowledge about some aspect of human sexuality. Take the Self-Assessment in Chapter 1. Did the assessment tell you anything about yourself?

You've probably noticed that there are quotations along the margin of the textbook. These are meant to be thought provoking. Write down the most interesting margin quote you've read so far.

We have carefully selected the photographs, charts, and tables to reinforce chapter material. On which page do you find the most interesting photograph in this chapter? Why do you find it interesting?

Because this textbook is based on scholarly research, you'll find that after we present important ideas or research findings we cite (identify) the source of our statements. These citations follow the style recommend by the American Psychological Association. The citations are placed in parentheses, with the author's name and date of publication, i.e., (Strong and DeVault, 1994). You will find the full bibliographic citation for these sources at the back of the textbook in the bibliography. Find the first citation in Chapter 1 and look it up in the bibliography. What is its full bibliographic citation?

We have created a detailed index to help you find your way around in this textbook. Look up a couple of topics that interest you in the index, note down their page references, and then turn to those pages in the text. What were the topics you looked up?

Finally, list the three most important things you learned about human sexuality or yourself after reading this chapter.

USING THE TEXTBOOK

Each chapter is composed of several elements. There are some strategies you may use to make studying each chapter more effective. First, however, read the Prologue, which provides you with an important introduction to this course and the textbook.

Each chapter begins with a self-quiz. You can test your knowledge about the chapter material by answering the ten non-graded questions. You'll find the answers at the bottom of the same page.

Outlines are found at the beginning of the chapter text. Review the outline, then take a couple of minutes to browse through the chapter. Then turn to the summary at the end of the chapter. Read the summary to give you a sense of the main ideas found in the chapter.

Next begin reading the chapter in sections. Take a brief break or stretch in between sections. You'll find yourself better able to comprehend and remember the material if you don't try to read the entire chapter in one sitting without any kind of break. After you complete a section, review what you read before beginning the next section. At this time, you may wish to take notes. Taking notes serves two purposes: (1) The process reinforces what you have just read, making it more likely that you will remember and understand the material, and (2) it will make it easier to review for examinations.

Within the text there are key terms printed in boldface where they are defined. Include these terms in your notes.

After you have completed reading the main text, review the summary again. Key terms are italicized in the summary. Following the summary is a list of the key terms. Review the key terms to make sure you know their meaning. (They are also defined at the end of the textbook in the glossary.)

At this point, you may wish to read the Perspectives and Self-Assessments. Perspectives and Self-Assessments are found in boxes within the text.

If there are topics you wish to explore in greater depth, check the index for other places where they are discussed in the textbook. The Suggested Readings toward the end of the chapter may also be useful. If you'd like to know more about specific topics in the text, note the citation or reference found in parentheses—such as (Garber, 1992)—and look it up in the bibliography at the end of the textbook. You may use the bibliographic reference to look up the original article or book. Your instructor or reference librarian also can be of great assistance.

GENDER AND SEXUAL IDENTITY: AN EXPLANATION

Though the goals and objectives of each human sexuality course differ, one theme that unites all of them is the application of the information and concepts presented in class to students' attitudes, beliefs, value, and behavior.

We are aware that in asking you to describe the various influences of your personal sexual identity and the impact they have on your sexual attitudes and behaviors, a variety of challenges and obstacles may arise. First is the confusion that results from the barrage of conflicting messages and their interpretations. Second are the uncomfortable and sometimes painful feelings that may result from articulating and confronting certain experiences, perhaps for the first time. A third is the discomfort that occurs from revealing such personal issues to a stranger, that is, the instructor, for the purpose of receiving a grade. And fourth is the issue of how to proceed with your life once this information has been revealed. Hopefully, doing this exercise will give you a chance to clarify your feelings and reduce the confusion and discomfort that may be associated with self-exploration. The support and encouragement of your instructor and close friends as well as the services of the university's counseling center may also be helpful if you find that responding to the statements unleashes feelings that are difficult for you to deal with. Above all, you have the right to choose whether or not to participate or proceed. If you choose not to, consider putting the questions aside until a later date when you are ready.

In spite of these profound issues, we have, over the years of teaching human sexuality courses, found this assignment to be the most valuable experience of our students' semester. Students who choose to participate report insights that, they say, would not otherwise have occurred. Though many have discovered that it is no easy task to break the patterns and deeply ingrained beliefs that they have held since childhood, this exercise encourages them to consciously work towards improving them.

One former student wrote:

> The assignment really pushed me to take a closer look at my inner self—at what my opinions and values really are, and how people and the society around me influenced my development without my being conscious of it. Things came up that I had forgotten about, and it made me realize that I had to face my problems. I never knew that such feelings of resentment, insecurity, and happiness were there. I know the things I learned here will be beneficial to me throughout my life.

Begin by answering the questions on pages 8 and 9. Not all of these questions are appropriate for everyone's situation, so you can be selective in your responses. Next, complete the questions that appear at the end of each chapter after you've read the chapter in your textbook and finished the other exercises. Conclude this assignment by summarizing key elements of your gender and sexual identity according to the essay description on page 7.

If you choose to take the opportunity that this self-exploration activity provides, we believe that a meaningful dimension of this course will be fulfilled.

Notice that personal statements written by students follow each chapter's gender and sexual identity assignment. Students allowed us to use these quotes in the study guide because they agreed that sharing them may help increase other people's awareness and sensitivity to sexual identity issues. We hope you find them helpful.

GENDER AND SEXUAL IDENTITY ESSAY

As you go through the study guide, you will have the opportunity to answer the gender and sexual identity questions at the end of each chapter. This will give you a chance to look at both conscious and subconscious behaviors and beliefs and both the positive and negative experiences that have directly or indirectly had an influence on your personal sexual identity.

After doing these pages, you may want to write an essay to help you put all this material about yourself together. You can organize it by looking at some of these issues that may have been important to you:

- religious upbringing
- school/educational experiences and/or teachers
- peers or friends
- the media (music, TV, magazines, movies, etc.)
- parents and family
- cultural or ethnic background (including travel)
- other aspects, such as past relationships

Depending on how much exposure you have had to psychology, you may find it helpful to relate the following core issues in people's lives to the above areas:

- control/power and boundaries
- trust
- being real
- low self-esteem
- codependency and boundaries
- fear of rejection/abandonment
- neglecting personal needs
- grieving for ungrieved losses
- difficulty resolving conflicts
- high tolerance of inappropriate behavior, enabling, and boundaries
- difficulty giving and receiving love or being intimate

Your essay should address the impact each of these areas had on you in your earliest recollections and how these experiences and observations affect you now.

The conclusion should summarize key positive and negative experiences and possible constructive ways one can, should, or does cope with negative experiences to help reshape a more positive sexual identity.

Title your essay. Try to find an interesting and creative title that reflects your key issue, challenges, or successes. Past titles from our students have been "To Be or Not To Be," "Caught Between Two Cultures," "Being Taught to Hate . . . Yourself," "The Long and Winding Road," "A Girl With Curls," and "Family, Friends, Faith, and Fairy Tales." Use your imagination!

BACKGROUND INFORMATION FOR GENDER AND SEXUAL IDENTITY

1. My age is _______.

2. My gender is: Male _______ Female _______

3. My birth order is ____________________ (oldest, youngest, middle, only child).

4. The number of siblings in my family are: Brothers _____ Sisters _____

   Step brothers _____ Step sisters _____

5. My parents are: Married _____ Divorced _____ Separated _____

   Deceased (one or both parents) _____ Never married _____

6. My feelings about my parents' marital status are ____.

7. My marital status is: Single _____ Cohabitating _____ Engaged _____ Married _____

   Divorced or separated _____ Widowed _____

8. My feelings about my marital status are ____.

9. I AM _______ AM NOT _______ sexually active.

10. My feelings about this include ____.

11. My sexual orientation is ____.

12. My living arrangements involve ____.

13. The relationship I value most is with __________________

    because ____.

14. The relationship I value least is with __________________

    because ____.

15. My ethnic background on my mother's side is ____.

16. This has affected me by ____.

17. My ethnic background on my father's side is ____.

18. This has affected me by ____.

19. Concerning my ethnic background, I feel ____.

20. I would describe my parents' marital relationship as being ____.

21. My parents' sexual relationship is probably ____.

22. The impact my parents' marital and sexual relationship has had on me includes ________________________.

23. Concerning my sexuality, the expectations that my parents have had for me include ________________.

24. I have fulfilled some of these expectations by ____.

25. I have not fulfilled some of these because ____.

26. Concerning my parents' expectations of me, I feel ____.

27. In relation to my parents' sexual values, I feel ____.

28. I have handled these differences by ____.

29. I would describe my relationship with my mother as being ________________________________.

30. I would describe my relationship with my father as being ________________________________.

31. I would describe my relationship with another significant authority figure as being ________________.

32. My religious training was ____.

33. My current religion is ____.

34. I handle any difference between my parents' religious teachings and my own practices and beliefs by

____.

35. Religion has brought to my life ____.

36. The most significant factor that has influenced my sexual being is ________________________.

(Keep these questions and refer back to them throughout your self-exploration.)

RESOURCES FOR READING AND WRITING ABOUT HUMAN SEXUALITY

READING A JOURNAL ARTICLE

Academic journals are among the most reliable sources for information about human sexuality. The articles in such journals are scholarly and well-researched. Furthermore, the articles are generally reviewed by academic peers to ensure their scholarliness and accuracy. They should, nevertheless, be read critically as they may contain errors or inadequately substantiated conclusions. Chapter 2 of the textbook will help you critically evaluate the article.

The most important journals devoted to sex research are *Archives of Sexual Behavior, Family Planning Perspectives, Journal of the History of Sexuality, Journal of Homosexuality, Journal of Psychology and Human Sexuality, Journal of Sex Research, Journal of Sex and Marital Therapy,* and *Journal of Social Work and Human Sexuality.*

The Structure of Scholarly Articles

Scholarly articles generally have six sections: Abstract, Introduction, Methods, Results, Discussion, References. These sections may be briefly described as follows:

Abstract—summarizes the article. It briefly gives you the hypothesis, theories, methodology, results, and interpretation of the findings.

Introduction—discusses the topic, reviews previous research, and states the study's hypothesis and predictions.

Methods—describes how the research was conducted. It is usually broken up into three sections: (1) Subjects, describing the people studied; (2) Materials, describing materials used in the study; and (3) Procedure, describing how the study was done.

Results—gives the results of the research. It provides the statistics and quantitative results.

Discussion—refers to ideas, hypotheses, and studies examined in the Introduction; it also suggests future research or argues for or against a theory.

References—provides a bibliography of the article's sources.

Useful Reading Tips

1. *Read the Abstract first.* The abstract gives you a general idea of what to expect.
2. *Scan the article.* This will give you a feel for what is being covered.
3. *Skip around.* You don't have to read the article in any particular order. Reading the Introduction and Discussion sections first often makes it easier to understand the article.
4. *Read the article at least twice.* Don't think that something is wrong with you if you don't understand everything after the first reading. Scholarly articles are difficult.
5. *Read the Methods and Results sections for general information.* Usually all you need to know from these sections is how the research was conducted and what its results were. You usually don't need to know every detail.
6. *Think critically.* Just because an article is scholarly doesn't mean it is without errors or biases. Its research, for example, may not support its conclusions.

Evaluating the Article

In evaluating a journal article, the following considerations about research samples and methodological limitations should be kept in mind. Chapter 2 goes into greater detail about these issues.

Sampling Issues. The choice of a sample is critical. To be useful, a sample should be a representative sample, a small group representing the larger group in terms of age, sex, ethnicity, social class, orientation, and so on. Samples that are not representative of the larger group are known as biased samples. Most samples in sex research are limited because they depend on volunteers; their subjects are usually young, middle-class college students; and ethnic groups are generally underrepresented.

Clinical Research. A major limitation of clinical research is its focus on unhealthy behavior. Questions you should ask yourself include (1) what is the basis on which a condition was defined as healthy or unhealthy, (2) whether inferences gathered from the behavior of patients can be applied to others, and (3) whether the individuals are representative of the group.

Survey Research. Limitations of survey research include (1) people inaccurately reporting their sexual behavior; (2) interviewers allowing preconceptions to influence the way they frame their questions and biasing their interpretations; (3) the discomfort some respondents feel about revealing sexual information; (4) the interviewer's gender, influencing respondents' comfort level; and (5) the reluctance of some ethnic groups to reveal sexual information.

Observational Research. Limitations of observational research include (1) volunteer bias, (2) whether awareness of being observed affects behaviors, (3) whether participant observation affects objectivity, and (4) ethical responsibilities regarding informing those being studied.

Experimental Research. Concerns about experimental research include whether (1) the experiment adequately replicates real-life situations, (2) how devices used to measure sexual response affect responsiveness, (3) whether genital response accurately reflects sexual/erotic response, and (4) whether experimental results can be generalized to non-laboratory conditions.

Differences in sampling and methodological techniques help explain why scientific studies of the same phenomenon may arrive at different conclusions. Other times conclusions differ because of errors concerning different assumptions about human sexuality.

Journals

If we were to choose five journals with which to be stranded on a desert island (and still keep up with the field), they would be the ones listed below (alphabetical order). They should be part of your library's basic journal collection. (If not, see if they will acquire the missing titles.)

Archives of Sexual Behavior

Family Planning Perspectives

Journal of Homosexuality

Journal of Sex and Marital Therapy

Journal of Sex Research

In addition, other useful journals include those listed below. A few are specifically related to human sexuality, but because they are not usually found in college or university library collections, we have listed them here. Most of the journals are not directly related to human sexuality but often have relevant articles.

Adolescence

American Journal of Public Health

Family Relations

Hispanic Journal of Behavioral Sciences

JAMA: Journal of the American Medical Association
Jourlan of American Public Health
Journal of Black Psychology
Journal of Black Studies
Journal of Marriage and the Family
Journal of Marital and Family Therapy
Journal of Psychology and Human Sexuality
Journal of Social Issues
Journal of Social and Personal Relationships
Journal of Social Work and Human Sexuality
Journal of the History of Sexuality
New England Journal of Medicine
Sage: A Scholarly Journal of Black Women
Sex Roles
Sexually Transmitted Diseases
SIECUS Reports

WRITING A RESEARCH PAPER

There are nine basic steps to writing a research paper. The following outline will help guide you through the decisions you will need to make and tasks you will need to accomplish in writing a research paper. Notice that actually writing the paper doesn't occur until step eight.

Step One: Start with an Idea That Interests You. Begin with a subject, idea, or question that you find interesting. Because you may be spending considerable time working on it, make sure it's not boring. The initial idea may evolve into something entirely different. But you need to find a starting point.

Step Two: Make Sure Your Idea is Doable. Once you've found an idea that interests you, do some background reading to get a feel for the topic. See what research has been done. Talk with your instructor or teaching assistant to make sure that your topic is doable, that is, that it's not too general, there are available resources, and so on.

Step Three: Create a Bibliography. After you know your idea is doable, create a bibliography on your topic. There are several ways you can do this; two are use general bibliographies of scholarly articles, such as *Sociological Abstracts* or *Psychological Abstracts;* or do a search on computer bibliographic databases, such as PsycLit and Sociofile. Your reference librarian will be glad to assist you.

Step Four: Read Relevant Articles and Books. Read other work on your topic to find whether (1) your idea has already been researched, (2) other research changes what you want to do, (3) you can incorporate earlier research into your paper.

Step Five: Decide on Your Methodology. Decide which methodology you will use: survey, observational, clinical, or experimental. In Chapter 2 of the text you'll find a discussion of the different methods, which may help you decide on your methodology.

Step Six: Write an Outline. Writing an outline will help you organize your ideas and clarify the steps you will need to do in your research. Remember, however, that writing a research paper is an evolving process. You will probably change your outline as you go along.

Step Seven: Conduct your Research. At this point you need to conduct your actual research. This involves constructing the materials for the survey or experiment; planning how to conduct the survey, interviews, observation, or experiment; and collecting the data.

Step Eight: Write Your Paper. Use your outline to write a first draft. If you use the style used by the American Psychological Association, your paper will be divided into six sections: Abstract, Introduction, Methods, Results, Discussion, and References. These sections may be briefly described as follows:

Abstract—summarizes the article. It briefly gives you the hypothesis, theories, methodology, results, and interpretation of the findings.

Introduction—discusses the topic, reviews previous research, and states the study's hypothesis and predictions.

Methods—describes how the research was conducted. It is usually broken up into three sections: (1) Subjects, describing the people studied; (2) Materials, describing materials used in the study; and (3) Procedure, describing how the study was done.

Results—gives the results of the research. It provides the statistics and quantitative results.

Discussion—refers to ideas, hypotheses, and studies examined in the Introduction; it also suggests future research or argues for or against a theory.

References—provides a bibliography of the article's sources.

Step Nine: Rewrite. Rewriting is the key to good writing. After you've written your paper, put it aside for a few days, then come back to it fresh and re-read it, pencil in hand. (If you've input the paper on a computer, read hard copy.)

An excellent technique for refining your paper is to read it aloud. Reading it aloud will help you "hear" awkward sentences, bad grammar, incomplete sentences; it will help you "see" typos and misspellings.

Show your paper to a friend and ask for his or her reactions: Is the paper well organized? Is it complete? Does it read smoothly?

Finally, retype your paper. Be sure that you have corrected all typographical and spelling errors. A carefully typed or printed paper reflects the care you put into your project.

PART II

Chapter Outlines
Learning Objectives
Practice Tests
Observations and Reflections
Personal Involvement Assessments
Gender and Sexual Identity Questions

CHAPTER 1
PERSPECTIVES ON HUMAN SEXUALITY

CHAPTER OUTLINE

Sexuality, Popular Culture, and the Media
- Media Portrayals of Sexuality
- Television
- Hollywood Films
- Romance Novels

Sexuality Across Cultures and Times
- *Self-Assessment: Exploring Your Sexual Attitudes*
- Sexual Impulse
- Sexual Orientation
- Gender
- *Perspective 1: The Olympic Office of Gender Verification*

Societal Norms and Sexuality
- Natural Sex
- Normal Sex
- Typical and Atypical Sexual Behavior

LEARNING OBJECTIVES

At the conclusion of Chapter 1, students should be able to:

1. Discuss the dissemination of sexual images through the mass media, including men's and women's magazines and advertising.
2. List the different television genres and describe how each genre portrays sexuality.
3. Describe depictions of sexuality in Hollywood films, including gay/lesbian relationships.
4. Discuss and critique the main sexual themes found in romance novels.
5. Describe and compare the sexual impulse as seen among the Mangaia, Dani and Victorian Americans.
6. Discuss same-sex relationships in ancient Greece and among contemporary Sambians as examples of cultural variation.
7. Describe cultural variability of gender concepts, especially in terms of transsexuality and berdache.
8. Discuss the concepts of Nature and natural sexual behavior in relationship to societal norms.
9. Describe the emergence of the concept of normal sexual behavior, including the four criteria used to define it.
10. Explain the concepts of typical and atypical sexual behavior in terms of continuum and nonconformity.

PRACTICE TEST QUESTIONS

Multiple Choice

1. Advertising uses the sexual sell to promise:
   a. romance and sex
   b. popularity
   c. fulfillment
   d. all of the above
2. One of the leading sources of sex information for Anglo, Latino, and Native American male adolescents is:
   a. their female peers
   b. movies
   c. school
   d. parents
3. The social context of sexuality refers to:
   a. what behaviors are appropriate
   b. with whom certain behaviors are appropriate
   c. why behaviors are important
   d. all of the above are descriptions of social context as it relates to sexuality
4. The "Cinderella Legend" refers to:
   a. a set of rules that limits the amount of sex permitted to be found in romantic novels
   b. stereotyping of female roles in comedy shows
   c. music videos which titillate men
   d. a young woman whose heart was captivated by a frog
5. Gay men and lesbian women in film:
   a. are generally absent from mainstream films
   b. are consistently defined in terms of their sexual orientation
   c. are generally stereotyped
   d. all of the above are true
6. It has been suggested that reading romance novels may be a substitute for:
   a. reliable sex information
   b. actual sex
   c. pornography
   d. going to the movies
7. Most romance books:
   a. portray healthy images of sexual expression
   b. perpetuate dangerous misconceptions and/or stereotypes
   c. victimize men as often as women
   d. frequently involve the use of children as sexual objects
8. Culture:
   a. is a powerful force that takes our sexual impulses and molds and shapes them
   b. in America, appears to be irrelevant in shaping or molding our sexual behavior
   c. has its most profound impact on our sexuality when we are children
   d. is not subject to change over time
9. Marriage between members of the same sex:
   a. is recognized in 15 to 20 cultures throughout the world
   b. is universally condemned
   c. if condoned, is only done so between men
   d. is universally accepted by nearly all cultures

10. Which of the following ways of classifying sexual behavior is *not* considered to be a value judgment?
    a. natural-unnatural
    b. normal-abnormal
    c. moral-immoral
    d. typical-atypical

11. Sexual behavior that enhances one's satisfaction or sense of well-being is identified as:
    a. biological normal behavior
    b. conventionally normal behavior
    c. psychologically normal behavior
    d. morally normal behavior

12. The role of sex researchers is to:
    a. describe sexual behavior
    b. evaluate sexual behavior as good or bad, moral or immoral
    c. help the individual form ethical and moral judgments about sexuality
    d. establish cultural boundaries for acceptable and unacceptable behavior

True/False

Mark T or F on the line before the question.

____ 1. The media's portrayal of such issues as condom use, loving gay and lesbian relationships, and masturbation has kept pace with the wide range of other sexually explicit behaviors that are portrayed.

____ 2. Media images of sexuality permeate all areas of life.

____ 3. Mass media depictions of sexuality are meant to inform, not necessarily to entertain.

____ 4. Each genre has the same formula for what is sexually permissible and how to depict sex.

____ 5. What we have learned to call "natural" in our culture may be viewed as "unnatural" in other cultures.

____ 6. Culture is the most powerful force shaping how we feel and behave sexually.

____ 7. All cultures assume that adults have the potential for becoming sexually aroused and for engaging in sexual intercourse for the purpose of reproduction.

____ 8. The sex researcher Alfred Kinsey stated that normal sexual behavior is the sexual behavior a culture defines as normal.

____ 9. Popular culture only encourages sexuality.

____ 10. Sexual orientation appears to be malleable.

Fill-In

1. Mass media depictions of sexuality provide ____________________ rather than information.

2. Cultural rules or standards are otherwise called ____________________.

3. An immoral and illegal behavior that is a persistent theme in Gothic romance is ____________________.

4. Our incitements or inclinations to act sexually are called ____________________ ____________________.

5. In contemporary American culture, the only sexual orientation receiving full-scale legitimacy is

____________________.

6. The attraction to sexual partners on the basis of sex—male or female—is commonly known as

____________________ ____________________.

7. Within the United States there are approximately 15,000 individuals whose genitalia and identities as men and women are discordant with each other. These individuals are called ____________________.

8. Behavior that conforms to a group's average or median patterns of behavior that has nothing to do with moral or psychological deviance is called ____________________ sexual behavior.

9. Instead of classifying behavior into what are essentially moralistic normal/abnormal and natural /unnatural categories, researchers view human sexuality as characterized by ____________________

____________________, or diversity.

10. To understand our sexual diversity, researchers believe that the best way to examine sexual behavior is to view our activities as existing on a ____________________.

continuum	norms
entertainment	sexual impulses
heterosexuality	sexual orientation
incest	sexual variation
normal	transsexuals

Essay

1. Select and discuss how two of the various mass medias commonly depict sexuality. Discuss what is sexually permissible and how sex is depicted in each of the formulas.

2. All cultures assume that adults have the potential for becoming sexually aroused and for engaging in sexual intercourse. Select and discuss how one particular culture expresses their sexuality.

3. Name and briefly define three criteria that are used to decide whether sexual behavior is labeled "normal" or "abnormal."

ANSWERS TO PRACTICE TEST QUESTIONS

Multiple Choice

1. d
2. b
3. d
4. a
5. d
6. c
7. b
8. a
9. a
10. d
11. c
12. a

True/False

1. F
2. T
3. F
4. F
5. T
6. T
7. T
8. T
9. F
10. T

Fill-In

1. entertainment
2. norms
3. incest
4. sexual impulses
5. heterosexuality
6. sexual orientation
7. transsexuals
8. normal
9. sexual variation
10. continuum

Essay

1. Pages 9–24
2. Pages 24–33
3. Pages 36–37

OBSERVATIONS AND REFLECTIONS

OBSERVATION

Sex, Lies, and MTV

It is no secret that many people expose themselves to hours of MTV and other formats of music each day. What effect does this medium have on their sexuality?

Turn on MTV during key viewing hours (3 to 10 P.M. weekdays and/or 8 P.M. to midnight on weekends) to listen to and observe the messages that are sent through the television waves. Take at least 30–45 minutes of viewing time to record the following:

1. The titles of the songs
2. The artists' names
3. What was the message(s) in each song?
4. What images helped to convey the message?
5. What apparel was worn? How did the men's differ from the women's?
6. What kind of body language was used? How did it reinforce the messages?
7. What else did you notice?
8. What did you learn as a result of watching music videos?

Between songs and antics on MTV, commercials may also employ tactics that reinforce sex role stereotypes and provide calculated images of men, women, sex, and relationships. Carefully observe two or three advertisements while recording the following information:

1. What product was the advertiser trying to sell?
2. What images were provided to encourage vulnerability and/or desire for the product?
3. How were the men and/or women dressed?
4. What poses or images were used by the characters to sell the product?
5. What kind of background music was used?
6. As a result of this advertisement would you buy this product? Why or why not?

OBSERVATION

Everything You Wanted To Know About Sex, and Now You Can Ask

Each student comes to class with different expectations, needs, and questions. Naturally, this class cannot fulfill all of these, but it can attempt to meet the student where he or she is.

By filling out the following charts, finding out where each interest is located in the textbook, and then pointing out those unmet needs to the instructor, you can help the instructor fill in those areas that still need attention.

Topical Interests	Chapter in Text	Check Here If Not Found

Write down two or three questions that you hope to get answered over the course of the semester. Submit these questions, anonymously if you desire, to your instructor.

REFLECTION

"Firsts" in Growing Up

Throughout the course you will be asked to recall your own experiences and feelings about sex, growing up, relationships, and so on. The following list of questions is intended to give you the opportunity to explore your own sexuality and to begin putting the information that you receive in this course into some context.

Use the following questions as a guide but don't feel constrained by them:

- I first recall being a boy or a girl when . . . .

- What my parents told me about sex is . . . .

- For me, the experience of approaching adolescence was . . . .

- My family's reaction to my budding sexuality was . . . .

- I began noticing the same or other sex when . . . .

- The first experience I ever had that I would define as sexual was . . . .

- My attitudes about sex differed from my friends when it came to . . . .

- I think my sexual experiences have affected me by . . . .

- What I've learned about my sexuality from recalling my history is . . . .

PERSONAL INVOLVEMENT ASSESSMENT

PRETEST—WHAT'S YOUR SEX IQ?

Do this pretest before you start your reading in the textbook to see what your basic knowledge is about some of the many fascinating things you'll be learning about this semester.

(IT'S FUN TO TEST YOUR FRIENDS ON THIS!—AND SPREAD A LITTLE KNOWLEDGE)

Mark T or F on the line before the question.

____ 1. A female can become pregnant during sexual intercourse without the male having an orgasm.

____ 2. The time from testing positive for HIV and getting AIDS is at most 8 years.

____ 3. If a female is a virgin, she will have a hymen intact.

____ 4. A majority of the sexual crimes against children are done by adults who are friends or relatives of the victim.

____ 5. The volume of semen consists primarily of sperm.

____ 6. A female must experience orgasm in order to become pregnant.

____ 7. A female can become pregnant the first time she has sexual intercourse.

____ 8 Alcohol is a common cause of temporary impotence.

____ 9. An imbalance of sexual hormones is the most frequent cause of homosexuality.

____ 10. Among married couples in the United States, birth control pills are the most popular method of birth control.

____ 11. Male transvestites (men who like to dress in women's clothes) are usually homosexual.

____ 12. A large majority of parents want their children to be given sex education in the schools.

____ 13. A person must have symptoms of AIDS to infect others.

____ 14. The age at which puberty starts has stayed constant over the last 200 years.

____ 15. It is possible for a woman to become pregnant during her period.

____ 16. The most common sexually transmitted disease on college campuses is gonorrhea.

____ 17. A man usually expels more than 200 million sperm in each ejaculation.

____ 18. Fertilization of the egg (conception) occurs in the vagina.

____ 19. Less than half of the women with gonorrhea have any visible symptoms of the disease.

____ 20. Testicular cancer affects primarily men over 50.

____ 21. In all countries, AIDS is mainly a disease of male homosexuals.

____ 22. For most women, birth control pills have more benefits than negative health effects.

____ 23. Alcohol and marijuana are sexual stimulants.

____ 24. Teenage girls have easier pregnancies and healthier babies.

____ 25. Herpes simplex type II can be cured.

____ 26. RU-486 is a new type of AIDs test.

____ 27. Women can get pregnant without penetration of the penis.

____ 28. The HIV virus *can* be transmitted by oral sex.

_____ 29. Nocturnal emissions ("wet dreams") are often an indication of a sexual problem.

_____ 30. The amount of vaginal lubrication is a reliable indicator of a woman's sexual interest.

_____ 31. The practice of female circumcision halted long ago.

_____ 32. Most transsexuals feel that they really should be a member of the other sex.

_____ 33. Children first become sexual when they reach puberty.

_____ 34. Masturbation can be harmful if it occurs more than twice a week.

_____ 35. Statutory rape means forced intercourse between an adult and a teenager.

_____ 36. Most people who have had sexual experience during childhood or adolescence with someone of the same sex will become gay or lesbian.

_____ 37. People who live together before marriage tend to divorce less often than those who did not live together before their marriage.

_____ 38. Infants are capable of erection or vaginal lubrication.

_____ 39. The greatest increase in the number of people testing positive for HIV since 1990 is among white, gay men.

_____ 40. Oral-genital contact between husband and wife is illegal in some states.

Pretest answers and short explanations appear on the following pages.

ANSWERS TO PRETEST—WHAT'S YOUR SEX IQ?

1. True—The little bit of fluid that comes from the Cowper's gland before a man ejaculates can contain sperm and cause pregnancy. It doesn't happen often, but who wants to take a chance?
2. False—We really don't know how long it can take or if everyone that has the virus will get AIDS, but there are many documented cases of people carrying the virus for over ten years and yet not diagnosed with AIDS.
3. False—The hymen can be torn as girls grow up, and sometimes females are born without a complete hymen.
4. True—Most often it is friends and relatives and not strangers that molest children.
5. False—Most of semen is fluids from the seminal vesicles and prostate gland, so despite the fact that there are millions of sperm, it only makes up a small percentage of the total ejaculate.
6. False—A woman does not have to have an orgasm to get pregnant.
7. True—Sperm and eggs don't care if it is the first time. They meet and conception can take place.
8. True—Alcohol can cause temporary impotence. While it lowers inhibitions and makes us less likely to think of all the consequences, alcohol can cause physical sexual problems. The social expectations we have learned looking at sexy liquor commercials and billboards probably has a lot to do with the images and expectations we have for ourselves.
9. False—We really don't know why people are gay or lesbian, but their hormone level does not seem to be a factor. Recent evidence is pointing to genetics as playing a part.
10. False—Among married couples sterilization, including vasectomy for males and tubal ligations for females, is the most popular method of birth control.
11. False—Transvestites are not usually homosexual.
12. True—Surveys show most parents want schools to provide sex education; however, the people who oppose sex education receive a great deal of publicity in the media. There also is controversy about what should be covered.
13. False—You do not have to have symptoms of AIDs to infect others.
14. False—Over time, puberty has occurred at a younger age. Two hundred years ago menstruation started about age 17. We think it has to do with better nutrition.
15. True—While the risk is low, an egg can be put into her system at any time, and if it meets with a sperm, she can become pregnant.
16. False—The most "popular" sexually transmitted diseases on college campuses are chlamydia and genital warts.
17. True—Isn't that amazing!
18. False—Fertilization usually takes place in the fallopian tubes.
19. True—For many of the sexually transmitted diseases women, more often than men, will have no visible symptoms.
20. False—Testicular cancer is rare, and it affects men primarily from ages 20–35. Prostate cancer is the disease we see in older men.
21. False—In many countries, the number of men and women affected are equally divided.
22. True—While there are some women who should not take birth control pills because of their age or pre-existing medical problems, most women have more positive than negative effects.
23. False—In reality, alcohol and marijuana are depressants—but they do lower inhibitions as discussed in the answer to question 8.
24. False—Teenagers who are pregnant have higher risk pregnancies and more health problems. Unfortunately, they often don't get good prenatal care.

25. False—Though there is a drug that can lower the severity and pain associated with an outbreak of herpes simplex type II, the herpes virus stays in the body throughout a person's lifetime.

26. False—RU-486 is the drug to terminate pregnancy.

27. True—While rare, sperm deposited close to the vagina have caused pregnancies.

28. True—The virus that causes AIDS can be transmitted by oral sex when infected semen or vaginal secretions get into open sores or cuts in and around the mouth.

29. False—Nocturnal emissions are a normal occurrence in men.

30. False—While vaginal lubrication can be an indicator of a woman's arousal, it is only a *first sign* and further communication is important. Other factors like taking medicines can lower lubrication.

31. False—Unfortunately, female circumcision is still practiced in parts of the world.

32. True—Transsexuals usually feel like they are "trapped" inside the wrong body.

33. False—It is normal for children to masturbate and have sexual feelings beginning at a very young age.

34. False—Other than guilt that may be associated with it, masturbation does not have harmful physical or psychological effects.

35. False—Even if a minor is willing, statutory rape can be charged when an adult has intercourse with a minor. (In many states this law applies only to *minor women* who have sex with *adult men,* and not if the sexes are reversed.)

36. False—Studies show that many people have same-sex experiences while growing up and are heterosexual as adults.

37. False—Contrary to what was expected, people who cohabitate first are not less likely to divorce. It may not mean that these couples are unhappier than those that stay married, but rather that they tend to be less conservative than couples that don't cohabitate before marriage.

38. True—These are both responses that happen normally and naturally to infants.

39. False—At the present time minorities are getting AIDS at an increasing and disproportionate rate, and we are seeing more cases in women and infants.

40. True—Though not enforced, sodomy laws in some states ban oral-genital contact in all situations, including between married couples.

GENDER AND SEXUAL IDENTITY QUESTIONS

In the days of movie ratings, MTV, and computer-age technology, the influence of the media, for some, is overwhelming, dramatic, and profound. Try to recall how it has affected your attitudes and behaviors as you respond to the following statements:

- The types of media that influenced my sexual identity the most were . . . .
- The persons I admired the most included . . . .
- The images I tried to achieve included . . . .
- The media portrayed love relationships to be . . . . This affected me . . . .
- The media portrayed family relationships to be . . . . This affected me . . . .
- The most positive effect the media has had on my sexuality is . . . .
- The most negative effect the media has had on my sexuality is . . . .
- As a result of the media, my self-image and/or self-esteem was affected . . . .
- I became aware of the impact of the media on my sexuality when . . . .

Television showed me that if I had nice things that beautiful women would want me too. In one sense television also taught me how to have sex with women; not that I could see exactly how it was done but it gave me enough information to explore and figure it out. Television showed enough sex that it made me want to go out and try it myself. —27-year-old male Caucasian

We found the movie "Fast Times at Ridgemont High" on a movie channel. We were all so scared that our parents would come into the room that we kept switching the stations back and forth. We were all so excited because we felt like we were doing an awful thing. Nothing much ever came of it except that I will always remember it, being the first time I had ever seen two people have sex. —21-year-old Asian woman remembers what happened when she was 10

"Three's Company" made me think that sex was a nasty thing. The people on the show were always sneaking around, trying to hide something, so I thought that sexual curiosity was something that you should try to hide. —23-year-old Caucasian reflecting on how TV affected her views on sexuality as a young adolescent

CHAPTER 2
STUDYING HUMAN SEXUALITY

CHAPTER OUTLINE

Sex, Advice Columnists, and Pop Psychology
- Pop Sex Information and Advice as Entertainment
- *Perspective 1: Sex and Pop Psychology: Caveat Emptor*
- Evaluating Pop Sex

Thinking (Critically) About Sex
- Value Judgments Versus Objectivity
- Opinions, Biases, and Stereotypes
- Confusing Attitudes and Behavior
- Common Fallacies: Egocentric and Ethnocentric Thinking

Sex Research Methods
- Research Concerns
- Clinical Research
- Survey Research
- *Self-Assessment: The Kinsey Institute/Roper Organization National Sex Knowledge Test*
- Observational Research
- Experimental Research

The Sex Researchers
- Richard von Krafft-Ebing (1840–1902)
- Sigmund Freud (1856–1939)
- Havelock Ellis (1859–1939)
- Alfred Kinsey (1894–1956)
- William Masters and Virginia Johnson

Emerging Research Perspectives
- Feminist Scholarship
- Gay and Lesbian Research
- Ethnicity and Sexuality

LEARNING OBJECTIVES

At the conclusion of Chapter 2, students should be able to:

1. Describe the sex information/advice genre, its function as entertainment, and how to evaluate it.
2. List and describe critical thinking skills, including examples of value judgments, and objectivity; opinions, biases, and stereotypes; and egocentric and ethnocentric fallacies.
3. Discuss ethical and sampling issues in sex research.
4. Describe and critique clinical, survey, observational, and experimental methods of sex research.
5. Discuss and critique the contributions of the early sex researchers, including Richard von Krafft-Ebing, Sigmund Freud, and Havelock Ellis.
6. Discuss and critique the contributions of Alfred Kinsey.
7. Discuss and critique the contributions of William Masters and Virginia Johnson.
8. Discuss and critique the contributions of feminist and gay/lesbian scholars.
9. Describe emerging research on African Americans, including socioeconomic status, stereotyping, subculture, and increasing numbers of unmarried adults.
10. Describe emerging research on Latinos, including diversity of subgroups, stereotyping, and assimilation.

PRACTICE TEST QUESTIONS

Multiple Choice

1. The purpose(s) of media is/are to:
   a. sell more of itself
   b. entertain
   c. provide how-to information and/or moralize
   d. all of the above
2. The primary difference between the media and social scientists' research is that the media:
   a. may describe research in an over-simplified and distorted manner
   b. often qualify their findings as tentative or limited to a certain group
   c. must use critical information about studies in order to be accurate
   d. will usually quote only the most credible and reliable researchers
3. Basic to any scientific study is a fundamental commitment to:
   a. research
   b. objectivity
   c. ensuring that the hypothesis is correct
   d. applying the research to human behavior
4. Most of us experience sex:
   a. critically
   b. objectively
   c. subjectively
   d. romantically
5. According to the authors, of all the ethical issues surrounding research, the most problematic one is:
   a. compatibility with funding sources
   b. finding sufficient subjects
   c. the use of deception
   d. the interpretation of results
6. Value judgments:
   a. imply how a person ought to behave
   b. can be empirically validated
   c. provide an objective description of the world as it exists
   d. all of the above may be true
7. A major limitation of clinical research is its emphasis on:
   a. the physiological aspects of sexuality
   b. its use of experimental medicines
   c. its emphasis on pathological behavior
   d. all of the above are true
8. In the survey method for collecting sexual information:
   a. people tend to be poor reporters of their own sexual behavior
   b. the interviewers may be biased and subjective
   c. the respondents may hesitate to reveal information
   d. all of the above may occur
9. A critique of the research of Sigmund Freud includes his:
   a. puritan ethics and religion
   b. lack of ethics
   c. inadequate descriptions of female development and lack of empiricism
   d. biases against women and children

10. Who of the following first argued that both masturbation and female sexuality were normal behaviors?
    a. Sigmund Freud
    b. Havelock Ellis
    c. Alfred Kinsey
    d. Masters and Johnson

11. Masters and Johnson addressed and treated sexual problems by:
    a. using behavioral therapy
    b. suggesting shock therapy
    c. diagnosing and treating the underlying physiological problem
    d. classifying, describing, and treating the five stages of psychosexual development

12. Feminist research has focused and expanded the scope of information we have about:
    a. pornography
    b. victimization and child abuse
    c. sex and power
    d. all of the above

13. According to the American Psychological Association, homosexuality:
    a. is considered a psychological disorder
    b. is no longer considered a psychological disorder
    c. is considered an acceptable preference only if a person does not act on it
    d. the APA has no stand on homosexuality because the research is inconclusive

14. Values and behavior are shaped by:
    a. culture and social class
    b. our genetic pool
    c. strictly by discipline and control
    d. factors that we don't yet understand

15. For blacks of all classes, there is no such thing as:
    a. an acceptance of gay men and lesbians
    b. an acceptable form of premarital sexual activity
    c. an illegitimate or illegally born child
    d. a gender imbalance

Fill-In

1. A media genre that transmits information and norms about sexuality to a mass audience to both inform and entertain in a simplified manner is called a ____________________ ____________________/ ____________________ ____________________.

2. A term used to describe evaluations based on moral or ethical standards rather than objective ones is called ____________________ ____________________.

3. A personal learning or inclination that leads to selecting information that supports our views or beliefs while ignoring information that does not is called a ____________________.

4. ____________________ describes a predisposition a person has to act, think, or feel in certain ways towards particular things.

5. An ____________________ fallacy is the belief that one's own ethnic group, nation, or culture is innately superior to others.

6. The full disclosure to an individual of the purpose, potential risks, and benefits of participating in a research project is called ____________________ ____________________.

7. In the scientific study of sex, selecting samples that are not representative of the larger group are known as ____________________ samples.

8. A major limitation of clinical research is its emphasis on unhealthy or ____________________ behavior.

9. The method of research that uses questionnaires or interviews to gather information from a small group and makes inferences for a larger group is known as ____________________ research.

10. Sigmund Freud described five stages in psychosexual development, one of which refers to a stage in which a child exhibits interest in the genitals and is called the ____________________ stage.

11. Self-stimulation or erotic behavior involving only the self is called ____________________. This includes masturbation, erotic dreams, and sexual fantasies.

attitude
autoeroticism
bias
biased
ethnocentric
informed consent
pathological
phallic
sex information/advice genre
survey
value judgments

Matching

1. Krafft-Ebing _____
2. Sigmund Freud _____
3. Havelock Ellis _____
4. Alfred Kinsey _____
5. Masters & Johnson _____
6. Evelyn Hooker _____

a. First to use a large-scale survey/continuum to demonstrate the range of behavior that exists as it relates to sexual orientation.
b. First to explore the unconscious, leading to the development of psychoanalysis.
c. Was first to write scientifically about sexuality. Explored the origins of fetishism and sadism and found them rooted in masturbation.
d. Combined direct and laboratory observation with measurement of changes in the genitalia and began treating sexual dysfunctions.
e. An early English researcher who focused on women as being equals of men, re-evaluated homosexuality, and helped to redefine normal sexual behavior.
f. Demonstrated that homosexuality in itself was not a psychological disorder.

Essay

1. List and briefly describe five guidelines that can be used to evaluate the messages that the media presents to us.

2. Cite three ways in which our sex information may be biased or slanted.

3. Ethical issues are particularly important in researching the subject of sexuality. State four common issues that must be addressed and discuss why they are significant.

4. Describe why samples in sex research may be limited.

5. Select one ethnic group and discuss how culture affects factors in studying their sexual behavior.

ANSWERS TO PRACTICE TEST QUESTIONS

Multiple Choice

1. d
2. a
3. b
4. c
5. c
6. a
7. c
8. d
9. b
10. b
11. c
12. d
13. b
14. a
15. c

Fill-In

1. sex information/advice genre
2. value judgments
3. bias
4. attitude
5. ethnocentric
6. informed consent
7. biased
8. pathological
9. survey
10. phallic
11. autoeroticism

Matching

1. c
2. b
3. e
4. a
5. d
6. f

Essay

1. Page 50
2. Pages 51–53
3. Pages 56–57
4. Page 57
5. Pages 78–85

OBSERVATIONS AND REFLECTIONS

OBSERVATION

The Sexy Side of Magazines

Go to a library or through your own magazine rack and look at the lead or cover stories of popular magazines. Find one that deals with sex. Now quickly read the article and while doing so, ask yourself the following questions:

- Who wrote the article? (What were his/her credentials?)
- How many people were surveyed?
- How was the sample selected? Did it represent a cross section of the population?
- Was other research cited and if so, how reputable did it seem?
- Did the article make any sweeping claims?
- Given the above, do you believe what was said? Why? Why not?
- How did this article contribute to the marketing of the magazine?

OBSERVATION

Research Methods

To help you further understand the methods of research available, develop a chart of methods used to conduct sexual research and identify the advantages and disadvantages of each one.

Method	Advantages	Disadvantages
1. Clinical research		
2. Survey research		
3. Observational research		
4. Experimental research		

What, in your opinion, would be the best type of research design for each of the following questions?

1. What is the average age of first intercourse for Americans?

2. How do most people become acquainted at bars?

3. What are the effects of alcohol on sexual response?

REFLECTION

Who Participates in Sex Surveys?

Would you participate or contribute to a survey regarding your sexual behavior even if you were guaranteed anonymity? Why? Why not? If so, how honest would you be? Given your knowledge of, experiences with, and desires about sex would you tend to exaggerate or deny some information? How do you suppose your attitudes towards sex surveys compare with others who choose to participate? Given this, how valid do you feel sex surveys are?

PERSONAL INVOLVEMENT ASSESSMENT

LOOKING AT YOUR VALUES

Take a few minutes to complete the following values survey. There are no right or wrong responses. Answer as honestly as you can, and usually your first thought is most accurate.

Write today's date: ______________________

At the end of the semester there will be a similar list. The purpose of the class is not to change your values and opinions, but with knowledge and experience people often re-evaluate and fully embrace who they are and what they believe.

SA CIRCLE IF YOU STRONGLY AGREE
A CIRCLE IF YOU MODERATELY AGREE
N CIRCLE IF YOU HAVE NO OPINION
D CIRCLE IF YOU MODERATELY DISAGREE
SD CIRCLE IF YOU STRONGLY DISAGREE

FEMALE ________

MALE ___________

STATEMENT	LEVEL OF AGREEMENT
A. You should only have sex with someone you love.	SA A N D SD
B. Masturbation is a healthy, acceptable form of sexual behavior.	SA A N D SD
C. A woman should feel able to be as sexually assertive as a man.	SA A N D SD
D. Abortions should be available to any woman who desires to terminate a pregnancy.	SA A N D SD
E. Transvestites are psychologically dysfunctional.	SA A N D SD
F. Prostitution should be a crime.	SA A N D SD
G. Magazines like *Penthouse* and *Playboy* should be available at liquor stores.	SA A N D SD
H. Homosexuality is unnatural and immoral.	SA A N D SD
I. High school clinics should provide birth control.	SA A N D SD
J. All doctors should be tested for HIV, and patients notified of status.	SA A N D SD
K. Parents should be notified and give permission before their daughters can have an abortion.	SA A N D SD
L. All hospital patients should be tested for HIV, and doctors notified of status.	SA A N D SD
M. If a 15-year-old boy has consensual sex with a 20-year-old female, she should be arrested.	SA A N D SD
N. If a 15-year-old girl has consensual sex with a 20-year-old male, he should be arrested.	SA A N D SD
O. Surrogate motherhood should be legal	SA A N D SD
P. Rape is often charged because women regret what they did.	SA A N D SD
Q. A boy who has not had sex by the time he is 17 is weird.	SA A N D SD

After you complete the survey, look over your answers. Were your answers for J and L the same? Do you think the issue for these is the same or different?

Why do you think that?

Look at M and N. Was your answer the same?

Why do you think that you feel that way?

GENDER AND SEXUAL IDENTITY QUESTIONS

Even though gender issues don't directly relate to research, our ability to be honest about ourselves may be difficult when we're asked about sex-related issues.

If a trusted person inquired about our sexuality would you:

- be perfectly honest?

- be willing to reveal all of your prior sexual experience?

- share your medical/sexual history?

- discuss your sexual fantasies?

- talk about your painful experiences?

The most difficult sexual topic for me to talk about honestly is . . . .

If I was asked to share my sexual history with a researcher, I would probably . . . .

The written assignment really pushed me to get a closer look at my inner self. It is a great idea. I only wish that maybe we can do one at the beginning of the semester and one at the end to see the progress of our own development. —24-year-old Hispanic male

CHAPTER 3
FEMALE SEXUAL ANATOMY, PHYSIOLOGY, AND RESPONSE

CHAPTER OUTLINE

Why Two Sexes?
Female Sex Organs: What Are They For?
- External Structures (The Vulva)
- Internal Structures
- Other Structures
- The Breasts

Female Sexual Physiology
- Reproductive Hormones
- Oogenesis and the Ovarian Cycle
- The Menstrual Cycle
- Perspective 1: Relieving Menstrual Symptoms

Female Sexual Response
- Sexual Response Models
- Desire: Mind or Matter?
- Experiencing Sexual Arousal
- *Perspective 2: The Role of the Orgasm*

LEARNING OBJECTIVES

At the conclusion of Chapter 3, students should be able to:

1. Compare and contrast asexual and sexual reproduction in terms of genetic advantage.
2. List and describe the functions of the external female sexual structures.
3. List and describe the functions of the internal female sexual structures.
4. Describe the structures and processes involved in ovulation.
5. Describe the structure and function of the breasts.
6. List the principal female reproductive hormones.
7. Describe oogenesis and the phases of the ovarian cycle.
8. Describe the phases of the menstrual cycle and its interrelationship with the ovarian cycle.
9. Discuss menstruation, including cultural aspects, physical effects, and possible problems.
10. Compare and contrast Masters and Johnson's and Kaplan's models of the sexual response cycle.
11. Describe the psychological and physiological processes involved in the female sexual response, including the role of orgasm.

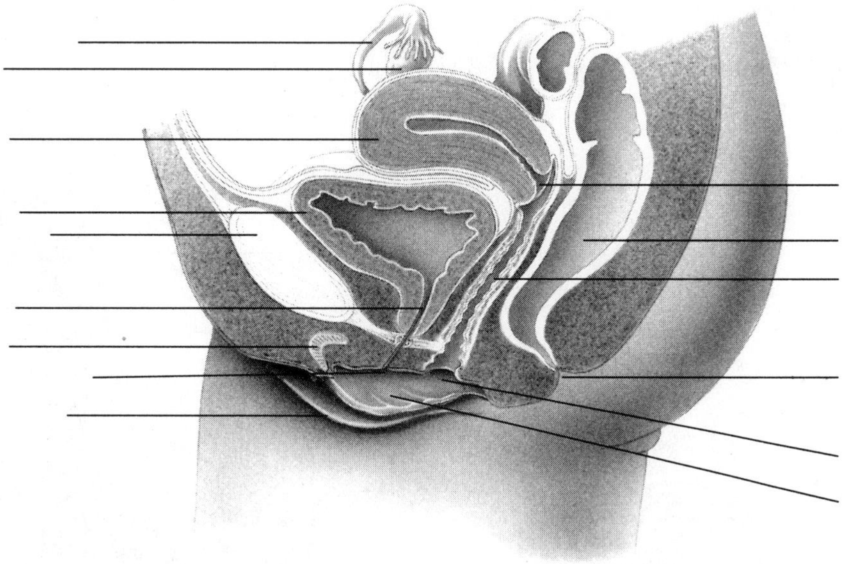

INTERNAL FEMALE SEXUAL STRUCTURES

Anus
Bladder
Cervix
Clitoris
Fallopian tube
Labia majora
Labia minora
Ovary
Pubic bone
Rectum
Urethra
Urinary opening
Uterus
Vagina
Vaginal opening

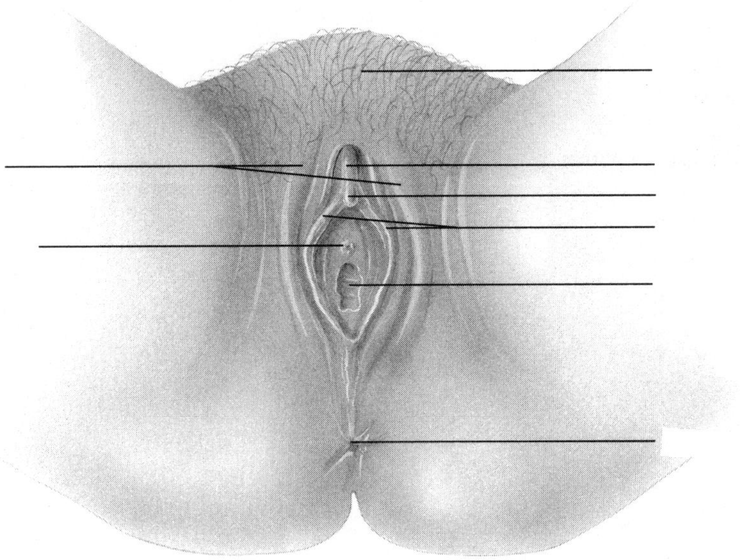

EXTERNAL FEMALE SEXUAL STRUCTURES (VULVA)

Anus
Clitoral hood
Clitoris (glans)
Mons pubis
Labia majora
Labia minora
Urethral opening
Vaginal opening

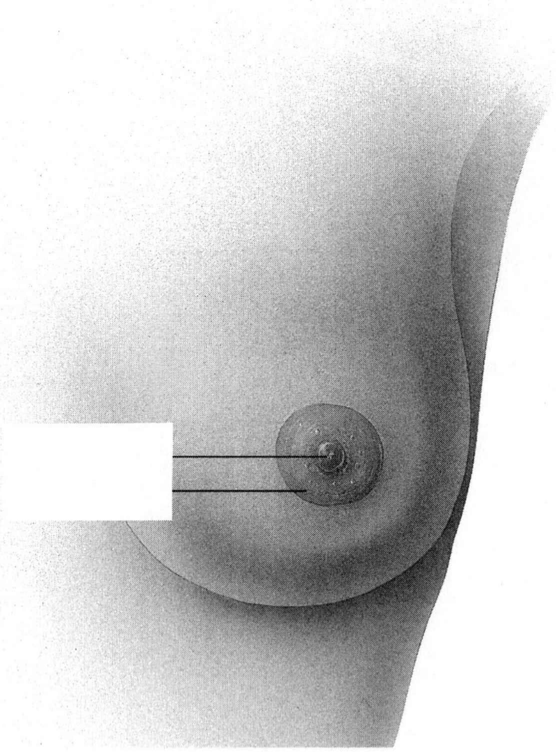

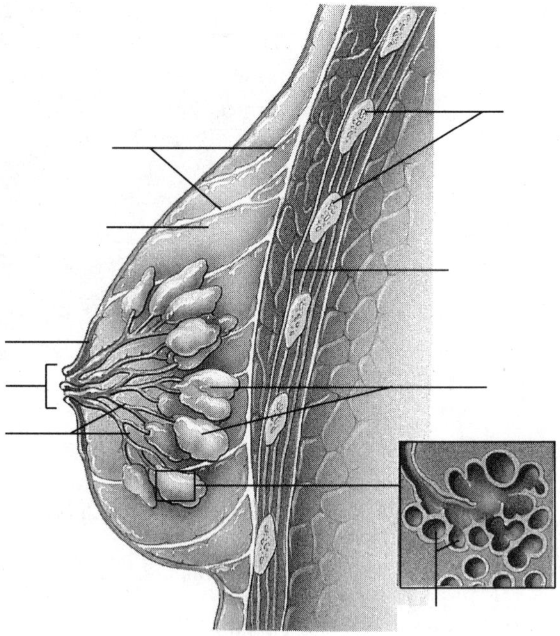

THE FEMALE BREAST

Areola
Nipple

Areola	Milk ducts
Chest wall	Nipple
Fat	Ribs
Lobes	Suspensory ligaments

PRACTICE TEST QUESTIONS

Multiple Choice

1. In addition to serving a reproductive function, the female sexual organs:
   a. appear exactly the same in all women
   b. bring pleasure to their owners and serve a role in human relationships
   c. provide a source of psychological pain for most women
   d. during sexual arousal, undergo no noticeable changes
2. The vulva consists of the:
   a. external female genitals
   b. external and internal sex organs of the woman
   c. labia minora and majora
   d. mons pubis and clitoris
3. The women who experience pain during their first act of intercourse tend to:
   a. be younger than those who did not
   b. hold more conservative sexual values
   c. expected intercourse to be painful
   d. all of the above are true
4. The purpose of lubrication during sexual arousal is:
   a. we don't yet understand what the purpose is
   b. to increase the possibility of conception and make intercourse easier and more pleasurable
   c. to attract sexual partners
   d. to decrease the possibility of conception and give a clear sign of readiness for penetration
5. The function(s) of the ovaries is/are to:
   a. release oocytes (eggs) and produce hormones
   b. continually manufacture oocytes and receive hormones
   c. provide a cite for pregnancy to occur
   d. simply release eggs
6. The most significant hormone that affects the maturation of the reproductive organs, menstruation, and pregnancy is:
   a. progesterone
   b. estrogen
   c. gonadotropins
   d. testosterone
7. Beginning with day one of the menstrual cycle, the sequence of the ovarian phase is as follows:
   a. follicular, ovulatory, and luteal
   b. ovulatory, follicular, and luteal
   c. luteal, ovulatory, and follicular
   d. luteal, follicular, and ovulatory
8. The shortest phase of the menstrual cycle is the:
   a. follicular
   b. luteal
   c. ovulatory
   d. they are all approximately equal

9. Premenstrual syndrome (PMS):
   a. is clearly defined by a cluster of physical and emotional symptoms
   b. is cured by the use of hormones
   c. has no generally accepted clinical definition
   d. occurs to nearly 90% of women who menstruate
10. Sexual intercourse during menstruation:
   a. may be highly pleasurable for some yet may carry health risks for women who have multiple sex partners
   b. though unpleasant for most, does not carry health risks for women who have multiple sex partners
   c. is taboo in nearly all cultures
   d. is a safe time to have unprotected intercourse because the threat of pregnancy is removed
11. Criticism of the Masters and Johnson model of sexual arousal is/includes:
   a. it does not account for the role of desire in sexual arousal and the plateau phase cannot be distinguished from the excitement phase
   b. it is accurate for men but not for women
   c. each phase should be described in more detail
   d. there is no criticism
12. Moderate amounts of alcohol and marijuana appear to enhance sexuality because they:
   a. increase hormone production
   b. act directly on the genitals to produce vasocongestion
   c. reduce the control mechanisms of the brain that act as inhibitors
   d. increase sperm production
13. The sex drive in both men and women is influenced by:
   a. pheromones
   b. testosterone
   c. estrogen and progesterone
   d. it is not yet understood what influences the sex drive
14. The first sign of sexual excitement in women is:
   a. sweating or moistening of the vaginal walls
   b. the tenting of the inner two-thirds of the vagina
   c. changes in the appearance of the breasts and genitals
   d. all of the above happen at the same time
15. Women:
   a. after experiencing the refractory period can once again achieve orgasm
   b. experience multiple orgasms regularly
   c. are physiologically able to be orgasmic immediately after orgasm
   d. must achieve orgasm to feel emotionally satisfied and fulfilled

Fill-In

1. The part of the female anatomy that contains a high concentration of nerve endings and is the center of sexual arousal is the ____________________.

2. Located on either side of the vaginal opening are two small ducts called the ____________________ ____________________, which secrete a small amount of moisture during sexual arousal.

3. The opening of the vagina is known as the __________.

4. The lining of the uterine wall that is filled with tiny blood vessels and is shed during menstruation is called the ___________________.

5. The release of an egg from the ovary is called ___________________.

6. Chemical substances that serve as messengers and travel through the bloodstream are called ___________________.

7. The pair of chromosomes that determine the genetic sex of the female is labeled ___________________.

8. Pelvic cramping and pain during the menstrual cycle is a condition called ___________________.

9. When women do not menstruate for reasons other than aging the condition is called ___________________.

10. Certain areas of the skin that are highly sensitive to touch and have erotic association attached to them are called ___________________ ___________________.

11. Chemical substances that are secreted and appear to arouse sexual interest are called ___________________.

12. Another term for sex drive is ___________________.

13. For both males and females, the physiological changes that occur during sexual excitement depend on two processes: the swelling with blood known as ___________________ and muscle tension known as ___________________.

14. For women, the first sign of sexual excitement is the moistening of the vaginal walls through a process known as ___________________.

15. The rhythmic contractions of the vagina, uterus, and pelvic muscles accompanied by intensely pleasurable sensations is called ___________________.

amenorrhea	libido
Bartholin's gland	orgasm
clitoris	ovulation
dysmenorrhea	pheromones
endometrium	sweating
erogenous zones	vasocongestion and myotonia
hormones	XX
introitus	

Essay

1. Beginning with the first day of the menstrual cycle, briefly describe the ovarian cycle, approximately how long each phase lasts, and which hormones play a significant role during that time.

2. Briefly describe and differentiate between the Masters and Johnson's and the Kaplan's model of the sexual response cycle.

3. Describe the physiological changes that occur during sexual arousal in women.

ANSWERS TO PRACTICE TEST QUESTIONS

Multiple Choice

1. b
2. a
3. d
4. b
5. a
6. b
7. a
8. c
9. c
10. a
11. a
12. c
13. b
14. a
15. c

Fill-In

1. clitoris
2. Bartholin's gland
3. introitus
4. endometrium
5. ovulation
6. hormones
7. XX
8. dysmenorrhea
9. amenorrhea
10. erogenous zones
11. pheromones
12. libido
13. vasocongestion and myotonia
14. sweating
15. orgasm

Essay

1. Pages 100–107
2. Pages 113–115
3. Pages 117–119

OBSERVATIONS AND REFLECTIONS

OBSERVATION

Looking at Media Images

While observing advertisements (billboards, photo ads, etc.), look for symbols and the presentation of the female genitals and the breasts. What is the link between these and female sexuality?

Discuss with three men and three women their ideas and perceptions about the size of female breasts. How do their views differ and what thoughts are shared?

OBSERVATION

Menstruation Attitudes

Because different cultures, genders, and generations view menstruating women from different perspectives, it might be interesting to find out how your partner, older relative, or friend from another culture view this. Keep in mind that each opinion should be valued and respected.

Before you begin asking questions, you will probably want to explain that you're taking a human sexuality course and are investigating different attitudes about menstruation.

A few sample questions that you might want to ask include:

- How is a menstruating woman regarded in your culture/generation?

- Were there any restrictions placed on a woman while she was menstruating?

- Was the frequency or pattern of sexual intercourse between a couple affected when the woman was menstruating?

- What are your feelings about sexual intercourse during menstruation?

- Ask a close women friend or partner if she experiences any discomforts in association with menstruation. If so, what kind? When and how does she deal with them? What are her feelings about menstruation?

OBSERVATION

Charting Cycles

Many women experience changes during the month that are related to their menstrual cycle. Keeping track of the symptoms they experience, especially if they suffer from PMS or dysmennorhea, can help them, along with the help of a health professional, to find patterns and solutions. The information they record can help indicate, for instance, whether birth control pills, diet changes, exercise, and/or diet treatment would be useful. Women whose symptoms are not severe may also wish to learn more about how their menstrual cycle affects them.

The following chart provides a list of the variety of reactions women may experience. (Men may wish to share this chart with a woman if they are in a close relationship and feel this would be appropriate. Otherwise, they can save it for a time when it might be useful.) Review the chart and if you choose to keep track of symptoms (preferably for a few months), answer the questions below:

- Did you have many symptoms that were moderate or severe?

- What time of the month did symptoms occur?

- Could symptoms be attributed to other events in your life, that is, stress on the job, school problems, relationship problems? Keeping the chart over several months will give a better indication as to whether the symptoms are related to events in your life or if they are indeed psychological.

Day 1 Date:
NAME: ____________________

Grading of menses: 0-none, 1-slight, 2-moderate, 3-heavy, 4-heavy and clots

GRADING OF SYMPTOMS
0-none
1-mild—present but does not interfere with activities
2-moderate—present and interferes with activities but not disabling
3-severe—disabling

DAY	1	2	3	4	5	6	7	8	9	10	11	12	13	14	15	16	17	18	19	20	21	22	23	24	25	26	27	28	29	30	31	32	33	34	35
MENSES																																			
WEIGHT																																			
Nervous tension																																			
Mood swings																																			
Irritability																																			
Anxiety																																			
Headache																																			
Craving for sweets																																			
Increased appetite																																			
Heart pounding																																			
Fatigue																																			
Dizziness or faintness																																			
Decreased coordination																																			
Depression																																			
Forgetfulness																																			
Crying																																			
Confusion																																			
Insomnia																																			
Weight gain																																			
Swelling																																			
Breast tenderness																																			
Abdominal bloating																																			
Cramps (low abdominal)																																			
Backache																																			
General aches/pains																																			

Prepared by DEL AMO HOSPITAL • 23700 Camino Del Sol • Torrance, CA 90505 • 310 530-1151

REFLECTION—FOR WOMEN ONLY

Looking in the Mirror

In a private location and in front of a full mirror, remove all of your clothes. Look at yourself from the front, side, and rear. Flex your muscles, slouch, and/or stand tall and *really* look at yourself. Do you appear firm, rounded, proportioned? What is the texture of your skin? Do you like what you see? How do you feel about your breasts? Shoulders? Backside? Legs?

Now, if you are comfortable, hold a mirror to closely examine your genitals. Can you locate each of the parts that were discussed and labeled in class? If you like, gently touch each part of your genitals. How does it feel? What colors do you see? Did you notice something new about your genitals?

When you are ready, reflect on this experience. How comfortable were you when looking at or touching yourself? Why did you feel this way? Are you pleased with what you saw and/or felt? Is there anything that you might want to do to change or modify your appearance? In an intimate relationship, would you feel comfortable sharing the feelings and experiences you have about your body?

REFLECTION—FOR MEN ONLY

Looking at Women's Bodies

Having viewed women's bodies, if not in person, then in a textbook, take a moment to evaluate your feelings about them.

How do you feel about the curves of a woman's body; the roundness of the breasts, hips, and buttocks? What is your reaction when you view the genitals? Can you locate each of the parts that were mentioned in the textbook? When viewing women's genitals, do you become aroused or are you simply curious? Do you find them attractive, unattractive, or do you feel neutral about them? What do you find the most and the least attractive about a woman's body? Would you consider sharing your feelings with a partner or a trusted friend?

EXERCISE—FOR WOMEN AND MEN

Take out two pieces of paper and on one draw and label the female genitals. On the other, draw and label the male's.

Which were you most comfortable drawing? How did you feel while drawing the illustrations? Would you have felt more comfortable drawing non-sexual anatomical parts? Save and review these drawings when preparing for the examination for the class.

GENDER AND SEXUAL IDENTITY QUESTIONS

(For Women Only)

- The first recollection I had about my body was when . . . .
- At that time, I recall feeling . . . .
- I began to menstruate when I was . . . .
- When this occurred, I felt . . . .
- I discussed this event with . . . .
- I have/have not experienced orgasm. (I'm not sure.)
- My first orgasm occurred . . . .
- I recall feeling . . . . when this happened.
- When I look at myself naked in the mirror, I feel . . . .
- When my partner looks at me naked, I feel . . . .
- What I like least about my body is . . . .
- What I like most about my body is . . . .

(For Men Only)

- I began noticing that a female's body was different than mine when . . . .

- At that time, I recall feeling . . . .

- My favorite part about a woman's body is . . . .

- My least favorite part about a woman's body is . . . .

I contribute a great deal of my negative body image and sexual identity to the constant pressures of my childhood. I remember that they (friends) always made fun of my tummy, saying I looked pregnant (even though I was relatively small). I CANNOT look in the mirror today without seeing this huge stomach, whether it exists or not; I cannot have sex without thinking that all this man sees is my stomach. People can tell me I am beautiful daily and all I can think is that if they saw me naked they would not think so. —27-year-old female Caucasian

I remember one day when I was about seven I was shopping with my mom. She bought Maxi pads and I asked her what they were. She said she would tell me when I was older, but she never did, and I had to learn about it from a friend. —25-year-old female of Mexican origin

I remember as if it were yesterday when I called my mom into the bathroom telling her calmly, "I started." My dad stood in the other room saying, "Oh boy, my little girl is growing up." I felt so proud because my friends had always told me that starting your menstrual cycle was a little scary and embarrassing but for my family it was a new beginning of adulthood and I felt very comfortable with the entire episode. —23-year-old Black female

CHAPTER 4
MALE SEXUAL ANATOMY, PHYSIOLOGY, AND RESPONSE

CHAPTER OUTLINE

Male Sex Organs: What Are They For?
- External Structures
- *Perspective 1: The Penis: More Than Meets the Eye*
- Internal Structures
- The Breasts and Other Structures

Male Sexual Physiology
- Sex Hormones
- Spermatogenesis
- Semen Production

Male Sexual Response
- Erection
- Ejaculation and Orgasm

LEARNING OBJECTIVES

At the conclusion of Chapter 4, students should be able to:

1. List and describe the male external sexual structures.
2. Discuss our culture's myths about the penis and compare these with myths of other cultures.
3. List and describe the male sexual structures.
4. Discuss the male breasts and other structures that may be involved in sexual activities.
5. Discuss male sexual physiology, including sex hormones and the male cycle.
6. Explain the brain-testicular axis and compare it to the ovarian cycle.
7. Describe the process of spermatogenesis, including spermiogenesis and sex determination.
8. Describe semen production.
9. Compare and contrast male and female sexual response.
10. Describe the psychological and physiological processes involved in male sexual response, including erection, ejaculation, and orgasm.

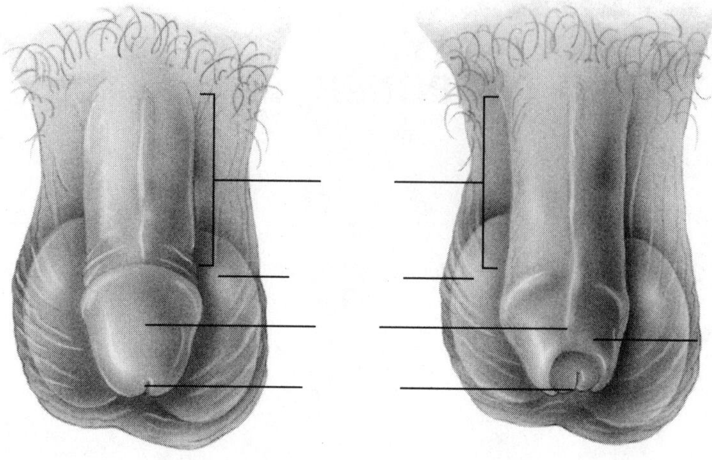

EXTERNAL MALE SEXUAL STRUCTURES

Circumcised
Uncircumcised

Foreskin
Glans
Opening of urethra
Shaft of Penis
Testes (in scrotum)

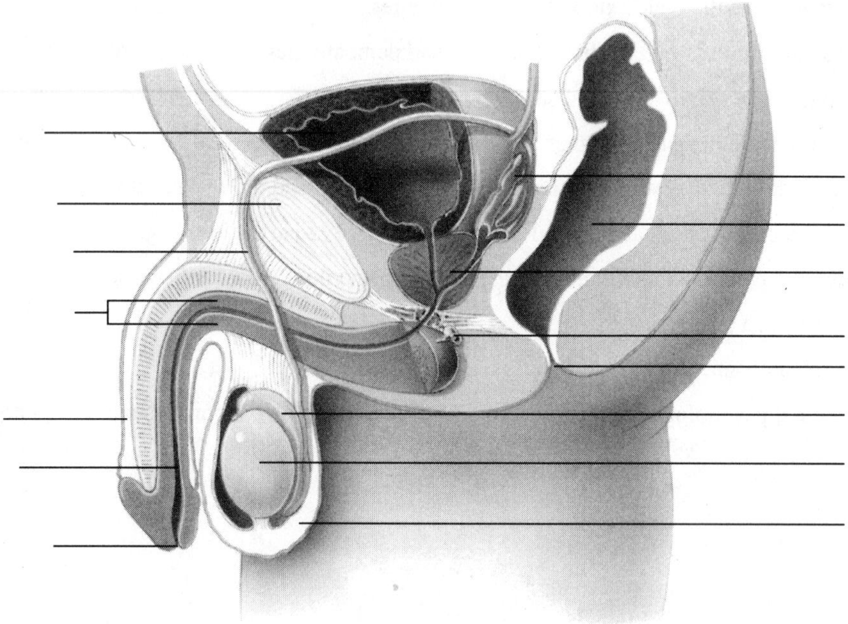

INTERNAL MALE SEXUAL STRUCTURES

Anus
Bladder
Corpus spongiousum
Cowper's gland
Epididymus
Opening of urethra
Penis
Pubic bone
Prostate
Rectum
Scrotum
Seminal vesicle
Testis
Urethra
Vas deferens

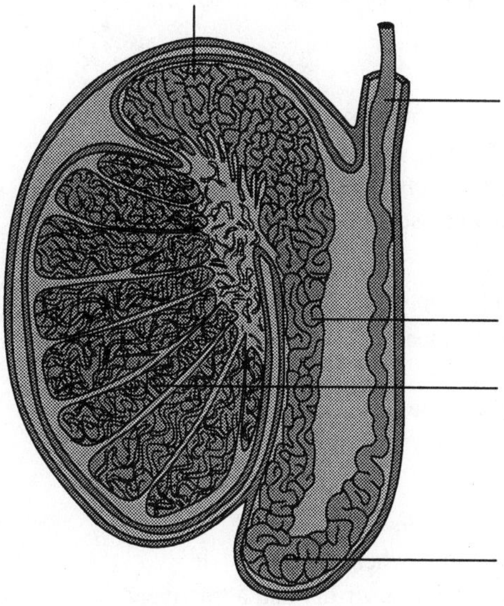

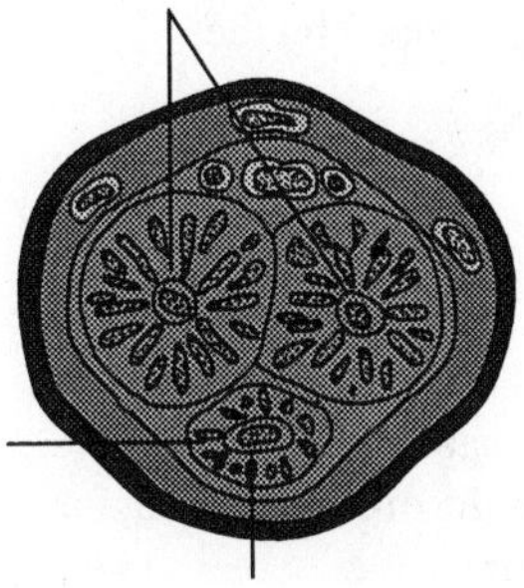

Underside of penis
(cross section)

CROSS SECTION OF THE PENIS AND A TESTICLE

Corpora cavernosa	Epididymis
Corpus spongiosum	Head of epididymis
Urethra	Seminiferous tubules
	Tail of epididymis
	Vas deferens

PRACTICE TEST QUESTIONS

Multiple Choice

1. In addition to a reproductive role, the male sex organs:
   a. continually manufacture and store gametes (sperm)
   b. manufacture and release testosterone
   c. provide a source of physical pleasure to its owner
   d. all of the above

2. Improper hygiene in uncircumcised men has been associated with:
   a. urinary infections and penile cancer
   b. urethritis and chlamydia
   c. genital warts and cancer of the foreskin
   d. evidence has not revealed any physical problems

3. Penile sizes:
   a. vary more in their flaccid state than when erect
   b. vary more in their erect state than when flaccid
   c. are an accurate indication of a man's virility and attractiveness
   d. are a significant measure of sexual attractiveness for nearly all women

4. The testicles vary in their appearance under which of the following conditions?
   a. when a man is sexually aroused or cold
   b. when a man is experiencing strong emotions
   c. when a man is urinating
   d. all of the above are true

5. The majority of the seminal fluid is produced by the:
   a. prostrate
   b. testes
   c. seminal vesicles
   d. vas deferens

6. The Cowper's gland:
   a. provides a major portion of seminal fluid
   b. helps to buffer the acidity within the urethra and vagina
   c. provides a cite for sperm to mature
   d. does not contain live sperm

7. Men may experience:
   a. regular fluctuation of hormone levels and mood fluctuations
   b. a dramatic fluctuation in testosterone production
   c. a rapid cessation of hormones, similar to that which occurs in a female during menopause
   d. pre-ejaculatory syndrome (PES)

8. Spermatogenesis, the production of sperm, takes in the:
   a. prostrate
   b. vas deferens
   c. seminiferous tubules
   d. epididymis

9. The purpose(s) of semen is/are:
   a. to provide an additional source of lubrication for penetration
   b. to provide sperm with a hospitable environment and means for transport
   c. to find and impregnate the egg
   d. to assure a partner that a man has achieved orgasm

10. Semen is relatively:
    a. acidic
    b. alkaline
    c. neutral
    d. varies depending on the health of the male

11. The penis consists of:
    a. spongy tissue
    b. muscle
    c. bone
    d. all of the above

12. The backward expulsion of semen into the bladder is:
    a. called refraction
    b. harmful if it occurs over a long period of time
    c. called retrograde ejaculation
    d. not associated with orgasm in men

Fill-In

1. On the underside of the penis is a triangular area of sensitive skin called the ___________________.

2. The operation which surgically removes the foreskin of a male infant is called ___________________.

3. Beneath the foreskin of the penis are several small glands that produce an oily substance called

   ___________________.

4. The manufacture and release of testosterone occur in the ___________________.

5. The hormone that triggers sperm production and regulates the sex drive is ___________________.

6. The ongoing production of sperm is known as ___________________.

7. Sperm are protected by the ___________________ ___________________ ___________________

   ___________________, which prevents antigens from developing, sperm from getting into the bloodstream, and provoking an immune response.

8. Seminal fluid, or the ejaculated liquid that contains sperm, is called ___________________.

9. The point at which a man feels a distinct sensation in which ejaculation must occur is termed

   ___________________ ___________________.

10. Following orgasm, men experience a ___________________ ___________________during which they are not capable of becoming erect or having an orgasm again.

blood and testis barrier	semen
circumcision	smegma
ejaculatory inevitability	spermatogenesis
frenulum	testicles
refractory period	testosterone

Essay

1. Identify where testosterone is produced and what its various functions are, beginning with the production of secondary sex characteristics.

2. Briefly describe the route that sperm take, beginning from where they are produced to when they are finally ejaculated.

3. Describe the two differences that exist between men and women during the sexual response cycle.

ANSWERS TO PRACTICE TEST QUESTIONS

Multiple Choice

1. d
2. a
3. a
4. a
5. c
6. b
7. a
8. c
9. b
10. b
11. a
12. c

Fill-In

1. frenulum
2. circumcision
3. smegma
4. testicles
5. testosterone
6. spermatogenesis
7. blood and testis barrier
8. semen
9. ejaculatory inevitability
10. refractory period

Essay

1. Pages 135–136
2. Pages 138–139
3. Page 141

OBSERVATIONS AND REFLECTION

OBSERVATION

Looking at Media Images

While observing advertisements (billboards, photo ads, etc.), look for symbols of the male penis. What is the link between this symbol and male sexuality?

OBSERVATION

Discuss with three men and three women their ideas and perceptions about the size of the penis. How do their views differ and what thoughts are shared?

REFLECTION

A friend of yours is having a son and asks your opinion about circumcision. How would you advise your friend?

REFLECTION—FOR MEN ONLY

Looking in the Mirror

In a private location and in front of a full mirror, remove all of your clothes. Look at yourself from the front, side, and rear. Flex your muscles, slouch, and/or stand tall and *really* look at yourself. Do you appear firm, rounded, proportioned? What is the texture of your skin? Do you like what you see? How do you feel about your breasts? Shoulders? Backside? Legs?

Now, if you are comfortable, hold a mirror to closely examine your genitals. Can you locate each of the parts that were discussed and labeled in the book? If you like, gently touch each part of your genitals. How does it feel? What colors do you see? Did you notice something new about your genitals?

When you are ready, reflect on this experience. How comfortable were you when looking at or touching yourself? Why did you feel this way? Are you pleased with what you saw and/or felt? Is there anything that you might want to do to change or modify your appearance? In an intimate relationship, would you feel comfortable sharing the feelings and experiences you have about your body?

EXERCISE—FOR WOMEN AND MEN

On one half of a piece of paper draw a picture of a man. On the other half, a woman. (Don't worry about your artistic ability.) Try to draw the picture before reading the footnote at the bottom of the page.

Research tells us that, typically, men's heads and women's bodies are emphasized. How does your drawing compare with the researchers' findings?

REFLECTION—FOR WOMEN ONLY

Looking at Men's Bodies

Having viewed men's bodies, if not in person, then in a textbook, take a moment to evaluate your feelings about them.

How do you feel about the angles and shapes of a man's body? His shoulders, waistline, and buttocks? Do you like body hair or not? What is your reaction when you view men's genitals? Can you locate each of the parts that were mentioned in the textbook? When viewing men's genitals, do you become aroused or are you simply curious? Do you find them attractive, unattractive, or do you feel neutral about them? What do you find the most and the least attractive about a man's body? Would you consider sharing your feelings with a trusted friend?

GENDER AND SEXUAL IDENTITY QUESTIONS

(For Men Only)

- The first recollection I had about my body was when . . . .

- At that time, I recall feeling . . . .

- I experienced my first nocturnal emission when I was . . . .

- When this occurred, I felt . . . .

- I discussed this event with . . . .

- I have/have not experienced orgasm. (I'm not sure.)

- My first orgasm occurred . . . .

- I recall feeling . . . . when this happened.

- When I look at myself naked in the mirror, I feel . . . .

- When my partner looks at me naked, I feel . . . .

- What I like least about my body is . . . .

- What I like most about my body is . . . .

(For Women Only)

- I began noticing that a male's body was different than mine when . . . .

- At that time, I recall feeling . . . .

- My favorite part about a man's body is . . . .

- My least favorite part about a man's body is . . . .

I didn't only have sexual experiences with girls during my adolescent years. I used to also play doctor with two of my best boy-friends. I don't remember it being as enjoyable as it was with the girls though. I used to go over to Eric's house and we would orgasm off the jets in his jacuzzi. This was long before we could physically ejaculate anything. —24-year-old Caucasian male

The summer of my eighth grade year I had my first ejaculation while watching a pornographic movie. I have never had a wet dream. I masturbated about four times a day until I was eighteen if I wasn't having sex with a girl that day.
—25-year-old male Caucasian

CHAPTER 5
GENDER AND GENDER ROLES

CHAPTER OUTLINE

Studying Gender and Gender Roles
- Sex, Gender, and Gender Roles: What's the Difference?
- Sex and Gender Identity
- Masculinity and Femininity: Opposites or Similar?
- Gender and Sexual Orientation
- *Perspective 1: Don't Judge a Man by His Lipstick or a Woman by Her Motorcycle Boots*

Explaining Gender Roles: What's Sex Got to Do with It?
- *Perspective 2: Machihembra: Rooster Now, Hen Before*
- Sociobiology
- Gender Theory

Gender-Role Learning
- Theories of Socialization
- Gender-Role Learning in Childhood and Adolescence
- Gender-Role Learning in Adulthood

Gender Schema: Exaggerating Differences

Changing Gender Roles
- Traditional Gender Roles
- Contemporary Gender Roles
- Androgyny

Gender Problems: Hermaphroditism and Transsexuality
- Hermaphroditism: Chromosomal and Hormonal Errors
- Transsexuality

LEARNING OBJECTIVES

At the conclusion of Chapter 5, students should be able to:

1. Define sex, gender, assigned gender, gender identity, gender roles, and sexual orientation and describe their differences from one another.
2. Discuss the evidence and implications for describing males and females as opposite or similar to each other.
3. Describe and critique sociobiology and gender theory and discuss the role of gender schema in creating or exaggerating female/male differences.
4. Explain cognitive social learning theory and cognitive developmental theory.
5. Describe gender-role learning from childhood through adulthood, including the major socialization influences.
6. Discuss traditional male and female gender roles and sexual scripts, including the significance of ethnicity.
7. Identify changes in contemporary gender roles and sexual scripts.
8. Discuss hermaphrodism and list the major chromosomal and hormonal errors and their relationship to gender identity.
9. Discuss gender dysphoria and transsexuality, including causes and transsexual surgery.

PRACTICE TEST QUESTIONS

Multiple Choice

1. Most gender differences can be traced to:
   a. gender role expectations
   b. male/female status
   c. gender stereotyping
   d. all of the above

2. When people believe that individuals should *not* have the attributes of the other sex, the result is that the range of human behaviors is limited by:
   a. gender role
   b. gender identity
   c. sex
   d. gender

3. Gender, gender identity, and gender role are conceptually __________ sexual orientation.
   a. dependent on
   b. independent of
   c. co-existent with
   d. related to

4. Those who hold negative attitudes about gay men and lesbians are more likely to:
   a. adhere to traditional gender roles
   b. be gay or lesbian themselves
   c. have had a bad sexual experience with a gay or lesbian person
   d. be liberal and non-religious

5. Cognitive development theory assumes:
   a. that children and adults learn differently depending on their age
   b. that children and adults have dissimilar brain patterns that cause them to learn differently
   c. that learning is a conditioned response that can easily change
   d. that environmental factors can alter brain wave patterns and thus facilitate or hinder learning

6. Peers provide information about gender-role norms through:
   a. play activities and toys
   b. verbal approval or disapproval
   c. their attitudes about various behaviors and beliefs
   d. all of the above

7. The *strongest* predictor of sexual intercourse among both males and females is:
   a. parents' modeling and teachings
   b. messages received from the church
   c. whether peers were sexually active
   d. statements and images from the media

8. Processing information by gender is important in many cultures because:
   a. multiple associations between gender and non-sex-linked qualities can be made
   b. they are a basis for norms, status, taboos, and privileges
   c. there is no importance to processing information in this manner
   d. a and b are both true

9. Expressions such as "men should not have certain feelings" or "performance is the thing that counts" are, according to Bernie Zilbergeld, example of:
   a. sex role ideals
   b. male sexual scripts
   c. gender role behaviors
   d. gender identity

10. Traditional female sexual scripts focus on:
   a. feelings over sex
   b. love over passion
   c. sex over feeling
   d. a and b only

11. American women are having __________ children than ever before.
   a. more
   b. fewer
   c. the same number of
   d. there is no data about this

12. Considerable evidence suggests that androgynous individuals and couples compared to sex-typed individuals and couples:
   a. have greater difficulty sustaining relationships and have lower self-esteem
   b. tend to have greater confidence in social situations and a greater ability to form and sustain intimate relationships
   c. have no differences in self-esteem or quality or quantity of relationships
   d. have higher self-esteem but poorer ability to form and sustain intimate relationships

13. Males or females possessing ambiguous genitalia are called:
   a. hermaphrodites
   b. transsexuals
   c. transgenderists
   d. transvestites

14. A chromosomal error affecting females who are born lacking an X chromosome is called:
   a. Klinefelter's syndrome
   b. Turner's syndrome
   c. a transsexual
   d. a pseudohermaphrodite

15. A treatment program for sex reassignment surgery involves:
   a. gender dysphoria therapy
   b. hormonal treatment
   c. living as a member of the preferred sex
   d. all of the above

Fill-In

1. Once a child's ____________________ ____________________ is established, he or she will often react strongly if you call a boy a girl, or vice versa.

2. Men and women are significantly more alike/different (circle one) than they are alike/different (circle one).

3. Divergences from traditional gender stereotypes are linked with ____________________ against gay men and lesbians.

4. The theory that asserts that nature has structured us with an inborn desire to pass on our individual genes—and this desire motivates much if not all of our behavior—is called ____________________.

5. According to cognitive social learning theory, boys and girls learn appropriate gender-role behavior through ____________________ by family and friends and by ____________________ or patterning their behavior after another.

6. According to Bem, the cognitive organization of the world according to gender is called gender ____________________.

7. Contemporary scripts, such as "both partners have a right to experience orgasm" or "sexual activities may be initiated by either partner" give increasing recognition to ____________________ sexuality.

8. ____________________ refers to flexibility in gender roles and the combination of traits to reflect individual differences.

9. The state of dissatisfaction individuals experience when they feel they are trapped in the "wrong" sex is termed ____________________ ____________________.

10. People who wish to have their genitals surgically altered to conform to their gender identity are known as ____________________.

androgyny	prejudice
female	reinforcement
gender dysphoria	schema
gender identity	sociobiology
modeling	transsexuals

Matching

1. sex _____
2. gender _____
3. gender identity _____
4. gender role _____
5. gender-role stereotype _____
6. gender-role attitudes _____

a. The gender we feel ourselves to be.

b. Being biologically male or female based on genetic and anatomical sex.

c. A rigidly oversimplified belief that all males and females possess distinct psychological and behavioral traits.

d. Masculinity or femininity; the social and cultural characteristics associated with our biological sex.

e. The beliefs we have of ourselves regarding appropriate male and female personality traits and activities.

f. The behavior that a person is expected to perform as a result of being male or female.

Essay

1. Explain how sociobiologists define and differentiate the attitudes males and females have toward sex and love.

2. Describe how gender theory describes the process of socialization and male/female differences.

3. List and describe the four very subtle socialization processes that children are exposed to during their gender-role development.

4. List three common traditional male and three female sexual scripts and briefly describe how each reinforces sex-role stereotypes.

5. List four ways that contemporary sexual scripts have changed for both sexes.

ANSWERS TO PRACTICE TEST QUESTIONS

Multiple Choice

1. d
2. a
3. b
4. a
5. a
6. d
7. c
8. d
9. b
10. d
11. b
12. b
13. a
14. b
15. d

Fill-In

1. gender identity
2. alike different
3. prejudice
4. sociobiology
5. reinforcement/modeling
6. schema
7. female
8. Androgyny
9. gender dysphoria
10. transsexuals

Matching

1. b
2. d
3. a
4. f
5. c
6. e

Essay

1. Pages 159–160
2. Pages 161–162
3. Pages 164–165
4. Pages 172–175
5. Pages 175–178

OBSERVATIONS AND REFLECTIONS

OBSERVATION

Actions Speak Louder Than Words

Turn off the sound of the television set and observe and study the mannerisms, behavior, and appearance of the adults that you watch. What characteristics are stereotypically masculine/feminine? How does the media reinforce gender-role stereotypes? Does any character in the program not concur with sex-role stereotypes?

REFLECTION

Gender Messages

Once again, try to recall the messages you received from your parents about being a boy or girl. Now imagine or recall the messages you might want to give to your children. What lessons would you repeat and which would you change? Specifically, think in terms of appropriate behavior, clothing, chores, amount of freedom, messages about sex, extracurricular activities, and/or career guidance.

Messages you would repeat:

Messages you would not repeat:

Are these issues ones that you might choose to discuss with your partner prior to having children?

REFLECTION

Advantages and Disadvantages of Being Male or Female

On a piece of paper that is folded lengthwise, write "advantages" on the left and "disadvantages" on the right. Now quickly brainstorm the advantages and disadvantages of *each* sex. When you are finished, ask yourself the following:

- Which of these is innate or genetic and which of these are cultural or have been learned?
- Which would you like to change? How might you go about accomplishing this?
- Which list is longer? Why?

If you have the time and would like to do so, share this activity with a friend, preferably of the other sex, and compare and discuss your lists. After you have done your list, you can look on the next page at lists we've collected from other students.

Advantages of Being Female

usually doesn't pay for dates
live longer, hardier as infants
lower cardiovascular disease rate
greater variety in clothing selections
can and does show more emotion/feelings; cries
is the primary "nurturer"
can be "everything"—mother, wife, professional
its acceptable to be a "little girl" or a "tomboy"
their arousal is more easily hidden (no embarrassing erections)
metabolizes and stores extra fat (warmth and softness
don't have to shave their face
no draft into the armed forces (yet)
less cultural pressure for job, money, education or to be a success
acceptable to be fragile or physically weak (or pretend to be)
generally, have a closer relationship with their children than father
receives many cultural courtesies; i.e., car doors open, "ladies first," etc.
can use menstruation as an excuse to be bitchy, emotional or irrational
may have the option to work or not to work
usually more intuitive

Advantages of Being Male

job superiority and higher pay
easier bathroom convenience, esp. outdoors
doesn't take long to dress
no shaving of legs/armpits
no periods & menstrual symptoms
no menopause
no pregnancy
natural to take aggressor role
almost always orgasms
no makeup
no birth control worries
"reputation" not at stake
variety of female partners as they become older
being breadwinner in family
body power, size
easier to detect STD
genitals prized, symbol of power and strength and superiority
less prone to weight problems
less sexual abuse (rape)
easier and cheaper to sterilize (vasectomy)
more freedom and independence as infant, child, teen, adult
fewer domestic responsibilities as child, teen, adult
can completely "retire" at 55
can age gracefully; looks "distinguished" with gray hair
braver, less fearful in dangerous or violent situations
can really relax when he comes home from work
can have expensive toys; i.e., cars, boats, motorcycles, etc.

**The authors thank Terry Frohoff for these sample lists.*

Disadvantages of Being Female

period and premenstrual symptoms
hard to urinate, messier
pregnancy, labor and delivery
weaker, smaller in size
makeup and dressing is more expensive
menopause
double standard of sexual conduct
job opportunities are less
weight watch—greater % of body fat
genitals thought to be ugly, shameful, dirty
household duties expected
must be "EVERYTHING"—mother, lover, friend, wife, professional, housewife, etc.
generally higher cost to groom, dress, and hygiene
shaving legs, armpits, etc.
usually has the full responsibility for birth control
generally unacceptable for her to be aggressive
often expected to "pay off" after a date
usually harder or taboo to initiate relationships
must be "lady-like"; no swearing
needs more time, romance, emotion and intimacy with sex
breast and cervical cancers
greater longevity might mean being alone after spouse dies
alone and vulnerable after a divorce
STD's and their symptoms less visible, hidden in female body
unequal pay for equal jobs
her reputation is always at stake (double standard)
has to be extra cautious (worries) about going out alone at night
career interference by pregnancy/children (no job leave guarantees)
her fertility potential and marriageability limited by her age

Disadvantages of Being Male

pays for date
can't show emotions
shaves face
longer working hours or years
less communication with children
has to be initiator
has to put up with female mood changes
higher cardiovascular rate (diseases)
expected to be strong, leader, father, breadwinner
expected to be macho/masculine to be accepted
can't have children or breastfeed
can't be feminine; play with dolls, do dishes, laundry, etc., without "criticism"
performance pressures (sexual and non-sexual)
the draft
expected to be the family disciplinarian "Mr. Bad Guy"
expected to be "Mr. Fixit": mechanic, electrician, plumber
can't hide arousal (tell-tale erections)
since he's usually the initiator, more subject to rejection
has difficulty with being physically warm, tender, or close in relationships; difficult to cry and show emotions, be intimate
often disciplined more severely
often judged by salary or status
custody battles, rarely gets custody of children, even if he wants them

REFLECTION

Pick Up the Papers and the Trash

If you share chores with someone in your household, list in the following chart those chores that you do and those your roommate or partner does. Put an "M" next to those that are stereotypically male and an "F" next to those that are stereotypically female. If a chore is neither, put "N." Now count those chores you do that are stereotypical for your gender. Who decided which chores are done by whom? List those you wish to give up and those you wouldn't mind doing and share this activity and list with your partner or roommate.

LIST OF CHORES

My Responsibilities	M, F, or N	Partner's Responsibilities	M, F, or N

Chores I'd like to give up:

Chores I wouldn't mind doing:

GENDER AND SEXUAL IDENTITY QUESTIONS

This chapter, probably more than any other, directly and indirectly touches on key factors that affect your gender and sexual identity. A number of these issues will be addressed in other chapters. For the sake of brevity and in order to avoid duplication, we will only address those issues which are emphasized in this chapter.

- I first recall feeling masculine/feminine when . . . .

- Because of/inspite of my gender, I was treated by my parents . . . .

- My gender role behavior has been most strongly influenced by . . . . They influenced . . . .

- My feelings about my gender include . . . .

- I present to the world a gender identity that . . . .

- Concerning my gender-role behavior, I feel that it works to my advantage when . . . .

- Concerning my gender-role behavior, I feel limited when . . . .

- I would like to change . . . .

In our house, my parents were very loving, at least around me, and therefore my first impressions were that love is one of the most important things in life. Loving yourself as well as others can bring a lot more happiness when you are able to express your sexual self without embarrassment or awkwardness. Now that I look back on it, my parents were more open than most in expressing what they felt was appropriate. Not only that, they were understanding and reassuring when it came to sexual questions and behavior. —27-year-old female Caucasian

Throughout my life, I have related much closer to guys than I have to girls. Being the oldest child, and needing to be responsible, I was much closer to my father and therefore I was more of a "tomboy" than most of the girls. I played softball, rode dirt bikes, played Army, and hung out with the boys all of my life. Even with this strong sense of being a tomboy, my identity as a female remained intact. I just felt that I was a girl having more fun playing boy games. Through having so many male friends I developed a better understanding of males and an understanding of how they thought about females. After starting high school, these male friendships began to change. I began dating on a more serious level, and I was not always considered one of the guys anymore. —20-year-old female Caucasian

I am not the totally masculine man, and as such, I can react with warmth and compassion and not be afraid to do "woman's work." I display the best human traits possible, whether the characteristics are considered masculine or feminine. —35-year-old African male

CHAPTER 6
SEXUALITY FROM CHILDHOOD THROUGH ADOLESCENCE

CHAPTER OUTLINE

Infant Sexuality

Childhood Sexuality
- Curiosity and Sex Play
- *Perspective 1: The "Origins" of Homosexuality*
- Masturbation and Permission to Feel Pleasure
- The Family Context

Adolescent Psychosexual Development
- Physical Changes During Puberty
- Influences on Psychosexual Development
- Gay and Lesbian Adolescents

Adolescent Sexual Behavior
- Learning to Be Sexual
- Adolescents and Contraception
- *Perspective 2: Sex Education Today*

Adolescent Pregnancy
- Why Teenagers Get Pregnant
- Teenage Mothers
- Teenage Fathers
- Reducing Adolescent Pregnancy

LEARNING OBJECTIVES

At the conclusion of Chapter 6, students should be able to:

1. Discuss psychosexual development in infancy and childhood, including sexual curiosity, sex play, and masturbation, and the role of the family in teaching children about sexuality.
2. Discuss current research on the "origins" of homosexuality.
3. List and discuss physical changes during puberty for both girls and boys.
4. Discuss influences on adolescent psychosexual development, including parents, peers, and the media.
5. Describe special problems confronted by gay and lesbian adolescents.
6. Discuss adolescent sexual learning, including masturbation, normative behavior sequence, virginity, and first intercourse.
7. Discuss adolescent contraceptive use, including the roles of erotophobia, lack of information, risk taking, and role testing.
8. Describe and critique contemporary sex education.
9. Discuss teenage pregnancy, including causes and motivation and the characteristics and needs of teenage mothers and fathers.
10. Describe the policy components for reducing adolescent pregnancy.

PRACTICE TEST QUESTIONS

Multiple Choice

1. Infants and young children are capable of:
   a. sexual arousal and orgasm
   b. sexual arousal but not orgasm
   c. orgasm but not sexual arousal
   d. none of the above

2. A child who is secure and comfortable with his or her body, including his/her genitals will:
   a. exhibit hypersexual activity, beginning at an early age
   b. be less vulnerable to manipulation and victimization
   c. more likely become pregnant at an earlier age than those who are not secure and comfortable with themselves
   d. none of the above

3. The state of human development when a body becomes capable of reproduction is called:
   a. hormone-induced
   b. puberty
   c. adolescence
   d. menopause

4. Much of what children learn about sexuality comes from:
   a. their innate awareness about sex
   b. observation of their parents' behavior
   c. teaching from their cousins
   d. their observation of animals

5. Which of the following is/are key factor(s) in preventing teenage pregnancy?
   a. parental concern and involvement
   b. parents' influence in instilling values
   c. a strong bond with parents
   d. all of the above

6. The authors contend that a viable solution to countering the sexual hype in the media is:
   a. to protect young viewers by censorship
   b. to eliminate the children's access to television and radio
   c. to balance the media with information about real life
   d. there is no way to balance the strong messages the media sends to children

7. Gay and lesbian adolescents:
   a. usually do not experience same-sex attractions until their late teens and early twenties
   b. usually have heterosexual dating experiences and feel conflict because they feel emotionally satisfied by them
   c. may feel their sexual orientation is an issue beginning as early as middle or late childhood
   d. embrace and celebrate their sexual orientation nearly all of the time

8. Masturbation:
   a. is a poor substitute for sex and provides no release from tension
   b. gives individuals an opportunity to learn about their sexual functioning and provides knowledge that can be shared with a partner
   c. is physically dangerous
   d. if practiced, is an indicator of a psychological dysfunction

9. Oral sex among teenagers has in recent years:
   a. become more frequent
   b. become less frequent
   c. remained the same over the past twenty years

10. When "giving up" their virginity, most teenage girls surveyed felt they were doing it because:
   a. of pressure by males
   b. they were in love
   c. they were under the influence of drugs or alcohol
   d. a and c only

11. Along with condoms, the method of birth control most frequently practiced by teens is:
   a. withdrawal
   b. birth control pill
   c. diaphragm
   d. use of a spermicide

12. Which of the following *rarely* exists in sex education classes for teens?
   a. fear-based education
   b. discussion of desire, pleasure, or sexual entitlement
   c. discussion of abstinence
   d. effective contraception information

13. In addition to the financial impact that teen pregnancies and births have on this country there may also be:
   a. higher risk for child abuse
   b. disrupted family lives and absent fathers
   c. limited health care and access to education for teenage mothers
   d. all of the above

14. The most pressing need teenage mothers have that can be provided within the community is:
   a. a pool of available men
   b. health care
   c. education
   d. b and c only

True/False

Mark T or F on the line before the question.

____ 1. Young people first learn about communication and gender role when they first reach adolescence.

____ 2. Many, perhaps most, children who participate in sex play do so with a member of their same sex.

____ 3. If a child's natural curiosity about their sexuality is satisfied they are more likely to feel comfortable with their own body as an adult.

____ 4. Research shows that most parents respond positively to their children's masturbating.

____ 5. Nearly one-third of girls and women polled about the onset of their menstruation did not know at the time what was happening to them.

____ 6. Kinsey called masturbation the most important psychosexual event in male adolescence.

____ 7. The single most powerful social influence on adolescents is peer pressure.

____ 8. During adolescence, young people are often too embarrassed to ask their parents about their sexuality and at the same time, parents are too ambivalent about their children's developing sexual nature.

____ 9. Unrealistic, stereotypic presentations of the roles of men and women appear to have no effect on the attitudes and understanding of those who view them.

____ 10. Gay and lesbian adolescents usually have heterosexual dating experiences during their teens but they report ambivalent feelings about them.

Fill-In

1. The psychological aspects of sexuality are otherwise referred to as ____________________ ____________________.

2. The authors point to research which stresses that children's sexual interest should never be labeled as "bad" but that it may be called ____________________.

3. The physical changes of puberty are centered around the onset of ____________________ in girls and ____________________ in boys.

4. Another term that refers to the onset of menstruation is ____________________.

5. Boys generally lag about ____________________ years behind girls in pubertal development.

6. An important psychological task of adolescence is to answer the question "Who am I?" One of the ways we discover who we are is by ____________________ ____________________, or trying out different roles.

7. The term used to describe the fear of sexuality is ____________________.

8. The biological stage when reproduction becomes possible is called ____________________.

9. The psychological state of ____________________ is a time of growth and often confusion, as the body matures faster

   than the emotional and intellectual abilities.

10. Both boys and girls may exert pressure on their friends to be sexually active. This is an example of ________________.

adolescence
erotophobia
homosociality
inappropriate
menarche
menstruation

ejaculation
psychosexual development
puberty
role testing
two

Essay

1. Briefly describe how, according to the authors, the experience of self-stimulation should be addressed with children.

2. What are two basic needs that should be observed regarding nudity in the family?

3. Discuss five factors that contribute to the lack of contraception among teenagers.

4. Briefly describe the multifaceted approach to reducing teen pregnancy.

ANSWERS TO PRACTICE TEST QUESTIONS

Multiple Choice

1. a
2. b
3. b
4. b
5. d
6. c
7. c
8. b
9. a
10. b
11. a
12. b
13. d
14. d

True/False

1. F
2. T
3. T
4. F
5. T
6. F
7. T
8. T
9. F
10. T

Fill-In

1. psychosexual development
2. inappropriate
3. menstruation/ejaculation
4. menarche
5. two
6. role testing
7. erotophobia
8. puberty
9. adolescence
10. homosociality

Essay

1. Pages 199–200
2. Page 200
3. Page 219
4. Page 224

OBSERVATIONS AND REFLECTIONS

OBSERVATION

Sexism in Toyland

Go through a toy catalog or visit a toy store to evaluate the differences between boy and girl toys. Which toys are for boys and which are for girls? How does the manufacturer differentiate between genders? What messages do the labels and packaging give to its purchaser (i.e., boys are action-oriented, mean, angry, and/or aggressive whereas girls are passive, play in small groups, and enjoy domestic tasks)? What types of activities do the various toys encourage (i.e., boys to be creative; girls to play cooperatively)? What percentage of toys are aimed at both genders?

OBSERVATION

The Sex Education Poll

Ask ten people and you'll probably get ten different responses to the question "What should be included in a school's sex education curriculum?" Sex education is, after all, one of the most controversial subjects taught in public schools today.

Find out from your friends and family what their opinions are about this topic and compare theirs to your own. Answer each of the following questions with a yes or no.

1. Should sex education be taught in school?

2. At what age should it begin?

3. Should 12-year-olds be taught about

   a. the danger of AIDS?

   b. sexually transmitted diseases?

   c. birth control?

   d. premarital sex?

   e. how men and women have sexual intercourse?

   f. homosexuality?

   g. abortion?

   h. practices such as oral and anal sex?

4. Should sex education try to teach

   a. moral values?

   b. that sex at too early an age is harmful?

   c. abstinence from sexual intercourse?

   d. the necessity of birth control?

   e. that abortion is an option when pregnancy occurs?

   f. that abortion is immoral?

   g. that homosexuality is just an alternative?

   h. that homosexuality is immoral?

5. Would having sex education make students

   a. more likely to engage in sex at an earlier age?

   b. more likely to practice birth control?

6. Should school health clinics

   a. make birth control information available?

   b. provide students with contraceptives?

7. Was your own sex education adequate?

8. How did you learn about sex?

   a. _____ sex education courses

   b. _____ friends

   c. _____ parents

   d. _____ other

Now check to see how your views and those you gathered from others compare with those of 1015 Americans polled from *Time* during November 1986.

Poll Results. Percentages are for Yes responses.

1. 86%
2. 23%
3. a. 95%
   b. 93%
   c. 89%
   d. 78%
   e. 76%
   f. 76%
   g. 72%
   h. 40%
4. a. 70%
   b. 79%
   c. 67%
   d. 84%
   e. 56%
   f. 44%
   g. 24%
   h. 56%
5. a. 24%
   b. 78%
6. a. 84%
   b. 36%
7. 73%
8. a. 9%
   b. 40%
   c. 23%
   d. 28%

Source: Jeanne Kohl and Jane Reisman, *Study Guide to Accompany Intimate Relationships, Marriages, and Families,* 2d ed.: 27–28.

OBSERVATION

Sex Education at the Library

There are many good books available from the public library that are designed to help parents answer children's questions about sexuality. Young children are curious about where babies come from and how they were born. Go to the library and check out one of the following books or a similar one for young children:

Banish, Roslyn (1982) *Let Me Tell You About My Baby.* New York: Harper & Row.

Gitchel, Sam and Lorri Foster (1984) *Let's Talk About..s-e-x.* Fresno, CA., Planned Parenthood.

Gordon, Sol and Judith (1974) *Did the Sun Shine Before You Were Born?* New York: Ed-U-Press.

Mayle, Peter (1973) *Where Did I Come From?* New York: Lyle Stuart.

Mayle, Peter (1986) *What's Happening To Me?* New Jersey: Lyle Stuart.

Sheffield, Margaret (1972) *Where Do Babies Come From?* New York: Knopf.

Sheffield, Margaret (1984) *Before You Were Born.* New York: Knopf.

Showers, Paul and Kay (1968) *Before You Were A Baby.* New York: Thomas Crowell Co.

Showers, Paul and Kay (1969) *A Baby Starts To Grow.* New York: Thomas Crowell Co.

Stein, Sara (1974) *That New Baby.* New York: Walker and Company.

Wabbes, Marie (1990) *How I Was Born.* New York: Tamourine Books.

After reading the book (they are very short!) answer the following:

- Do you remember your parents reading a book like this when you were young?

- If you didn't have a book like this at that age, would you have liked to? How would that have changed things?

- Would you recommend this book to a friend who has a child who is asking questions about babies? Why or why not?

- Would you use this book with your children? Why or why not?

If you have a chance and are comfortable doing this, show the book to your parents. Ask them if they would have been comfortable sharing this book with you when you were growing up. Ask them if they had a child now would they like to give them the book?

Did this exercise help you to communicate with your parents and hear more of their feelings about sexuality? Discuss their reactions.

REFLECTION

Advertising Gender Stereotypes

If you were a parent would you encourage or discourage gender-oriented toys? Why? How do or would you address the advertisements for toys that your children watch on television? When they are old enough, encourage them to note the differences in the advertiser's music; the dress, appearance, and mannerisms of actors; and the types of activities in which the actors are participating.

During hours that are targeted for prime-time children's viewing (Saturday mornings) fill-in the following chart. If you have children you could do this exercise with them.

Product	Appearance of Actors	Mannerisms	Activities	Comments

As a result of viewing advertisements directed at children I learned . . . .

REFLECTION

Answering Questions About Sex in the Tender Years

Consider the following scenarios. How might you react in each situation?

1. Your 6-year-old daughter enjoys masturbating regardless of where she might be.

2. Your 3-year-old son and his 4-year-old boyfriend are "caught" by you while playing doctor.

3. Your 8-year-old son asks you what "sex" is.

4. Your 15-year-old son asks you for money to buy condoms.

5. Your 15-year-old daughter asks you for money to buy condoms.

How might your parents have responded to these situations? How do your responses differ from your parents?

If you are comfortable, share these responses with someone close to you. How do they differ? How are they similar?

Try role playing the above activities with a friend.

GENDER AND SEXUAL IDENTITY QUESTIONS

Because a large part of who we are and how we feel comes from experiences and observations that occurred during our childhood and adolescence, more questions appear in this section than in others. Take time to fill out the questions below, perhaps responding to them over a few days time. Please don't feel limited to the questions or the format in which they are presented.

- When I was a little girl/boy, my parents dressed me . . . .
- The toys they gave me included . . . .
- I was taught to be . . . .
- I first recall being curious about the opposite sex when I was about __________ years old.
- My curiosity was satisfied when . . . .
  (I was not curious and/or my curiosity was not satisfied.)
- I began to masturbate when I was __________ years old.
- I recall feeling . . . .
- My parents' attitudes about my masturbating was . . . .
- Nudity in my family was . . . .
- My feelings about my sexual maturation were . . . .

- My parents acknowledged my sexual maturation by . . . .

- Concerning my sex education, my parents told me . . . .

- These conversations occurred . . . .

- I feel the impact of the sex education my parents gave me on my sexuality has been . . . . because . . . .

- During my adolescence, my friends and associates influenced me by . . . .

- My first sexual experience (which does not have to include sexual intercourse) with someone I was attracted to occurred . . . .

- Concerning this experience I felt . . . .

- The most positive aspect of my adolescence was . . . .

- The most negative aspect of my adolescence was . . . .

- From my earlier experiences I feel . . . .

(My friend) Chris was wild and most of all, a parent's ultimate nightmare. She was physically fully developed and aching to experience men and all that life could offer.... Because of her over anxiousness for both of us to break away from our parents and finally experience life, I got caught up in her exuberance and followed her lead. However, I was not yet ready to make this leap. To keep my friendship with Chris, I denied what feelings I had and learned to just go along with whatever mischief she had planned. —23-year-old female Caucasian

A good friend of mine and I (both 10 years old at the time) hung around each other all the time. We were so close to each other that we would sleep over at each other's house and after everybody would go to bed we would stay up and examine each other and touch each other's penis and watch it get hard. —27-year-old male Caucasian

I was in first grade and had received all "S" and "E"'s on my report card; I was sure to get what I asked for. Fidgeting in my dress, it was finally my turn to sit on Santa's lap. He looked at me and said, "So, little girl, what dolly can Santa bring you this year?" I earnestly replied, "I don't like dollys. I want a Super Cliffhanger Racing Tyco Glow-in-the-Dark Race and Track Set!!!" Santa began to argue with me. He told me that little girls don't play with cars, and that pretty little girls were supposed to play with dolls. I jumped off of Santa's lap and turned around and looked him straight in the eye and said, "I have 181 hot wheels, more than any other boy on my block.... Don't you remember me, Santa?" That Christmas, I got my Super Cliffhanger Racing Tyco Glow-in-the-Dark Race and Track Set. It appears I got my point through to Santa Claus loud and clear. —20-year-old female Caucasian

CHAPTER 7
SEXUALITY IN ADULTHOOD

CHAPTER OUTLINE

Sexuality in Early Adulthood
- Developmental Concerns
- Premarital Sexuality
- Establishing Sexual Orientation
- *Perspective 1: Bisexuality*
- Being Single
- *Perspective 2: The African American Male Shortage*
- Gay and Lesbian Singlehood
- *Perspective 3: Common Misconceptions About Homosexuality*
- Cohabitation

Sexuality in Middle Adulthood
- Developmental Concerns
- Marital Sexuality
- Extramarital Sexuality
- Divorce and After

Sexuality in Late Adulthood
- Developmental Concerns
- Stereotypes of Aging
- Male and Female Differences
- Partner Availability and Health

LEARNING OBJECTIVES

At the conclusion of Chapter 7, students should be able to:

1. Discuss premarital sexuality, including its increasing acceptance and the factors leading to premarital sexual involvement.
2. Describe the process of establishing a gay or lesbian identity and the different forms of bisexuality.
3. List the factors involved in the new social context of singlehood and describe being single in college and in the singles world, including the African American male shortage.
4. Discuss gay/lesbian singlehood and the significance of the gay/lesbian subculture.
5. Describe cohabitation among heterosexuals, gay men, and lesbians, including advantages and disadvantages and differences between heterosexual and gay/lesbian cohabitation.
6. Discuss marital sexuality, including frequency of sexual interactions and the significance of monogamy, reproductive legitimacy, and changed context.
7. Describe extrarelational involvements, including extrarelational sex in dating/cohabiting relationships and extramarital sex in sexually-exclusive and sexually-nonexclusive marriages.
8. Explain the different factors affecting nonmarital sex for post-divorce individuals and single parents.
9. Describe the stereotypes of aging, male/female and orientation differences in aging, and the significance of health and partner availability.
10. List the developmental concerns in young, middle, and late adulthood.

PRACTICE TEST QUESTIONS

Multiple Choice

1. Sexuality is a means of:
   a. enhancing intimacy
   b. enhancing self-disclosure
   c. physical pleasure
   d. all of the above

2. A commitment requires us:
   a. to value ourself a little more than the other
   b. to value the other person a great deal more than ourself
   c. to value the other as much as ourself
   d. to value neither and hope that love will prevail

3. Today, premarital intercourse among young adults in a relational context is:
   a. the norm
   b. not done by religious people
   c. unacceptable by most
   d. acceptable only if a person has been married once before

4. The most important factors in determining sexual activity in a relationship are:
   a. physical attraction and quantity of prior sexual experience
   b. level of intimacy and length of time the couple have been together
   c. inequality of power and a high level of permissiveness
   d. the availability of erotic films and a vivid sexual imagination

5. Acknowledging one's gay or lesbian orientation:
   a. involves rejecting the stigma that is associated with it
   b. usually occurs overnight but may take as long as a week
   c. is relatively easy because of society's acceptance of differences
   d. rarely involves a prior committed relationship with another person of the same sex

6. A large increase in the number of unmarried adults is primarily due to:
   a. the fear of pregnancy
   b. the lack of available pre-marital counselors
   c. the high incidence of sexual abuse
   d. the result of men and women marrying later

7. Research has found that involvement in the gay subculture:
   a. enhanced the likelihood of lasting relationships
   b. prompted men to avoid attachments
   c. has had no impact on the sexual activity of men
   d. leads to a decrease in self-esteem among gay men

8. Lesbians:
   a. have virtually no ties with the gay male community
   b. tend to value the emotional quality of relationships more than the sexual components
   c. form shorter-lasting relationships than gay males
   d. disdain the idea of parenthood and family

9. Cohabitation:
   a. significantly increases the chance for later marital stability
   b. significantly decreases the chance for later marital stability
   c. has not proven to significantly increase or decrease the chance for marital stability
   d. increases for women but decreases for men the chance for later marital stability

10. One important difference that exists between heterosexual and gay and lesbian couples is:
    a. gay and lesbian couples are less committed than heterosexual couples
    b. gay and lesbian couples tend to have "best-friend" or equalitarian relationships
    c. heterosexual couples emphasize love and are more romantic than lesbian or gay couples
    d. heterosexual couples are naturally inclined to settle down and start a family, whereas gay and lesbian ones are not

11. In our middle years, priorities, values, and practices may often change. These changes may include:
    a. family and work becoming especially important
    b. sexuality increasing in frequency, intensity, and significance
    c. a lower value being placed on intimacy between family members
    d. embracing the habits, boredom, and conflict that always accompany this period of life

12. Good sex depends on:
    a. good sexual techniques
    b. the quality of the relationship
    c. the prior sexual experiences of each partner
    d. a fantasy and a prayer

13. Researchers have suggested that extramarital affairs appear to be related to unhappiness in the marriage and to:
    a. premarital sexual permissiveness
    b. sexual intercourse at an early age
    c. gender; twice as many men have affairs as do women
    d. having a job which encourages travel

14. Which of the following statements is true?
    a. gay men and lesbians are such because they can't get a heterosexual partner
    b. gay men and lesbians sometimes recruit a heterosexual partner to become gay
    c. gay men and lesbians could change if they really wanted to
    d. none of the above are true

True/False

Mark T or F on the line before the question.

____ 1. The sole purposes of sexual activity are release of tension and physical pleasure.

____ 2. The more premarital sexual experience a person has had in the past, the more likely he or she is to engage in sexual activities in the present.

____ 3. Most gay and lesbian women have an easy time revealing their sexual orientation because of society's accepting attitudes towards sexual diversity.

____ 4. One must be sexually active or have sexual experience with the same sex in order to be labeled gay or lesbian.

____ 5. The majority of unmarried young adults under 30 live with their parents.

____ 6. Scholars suggest that divorce does not represent a devaluation of marriage, but an idealization of it.

____ 7. The decline in sexual activity among the aging is strictly biological in origin.

____ 8. Most extramarital sex is not a love affair but is generally more sexual than emotional.

____ 9. Single divorced parents are more likely than divorced women without children to be sexually active.

____ 10. Gay men and lesbians could change their sexual orientation if they wanted.

Fill-In

1. Traditional gender roles call for men to be ____________________-oriented and women to be ____________________-oriented.

2. The term used to refer to the sexual activities that occur primarily among unmarried, divorced, and/or widowed adults is ____________________ sex.

3. ____________________ ____________________ refers to sexual activities, especially sexual intercourse, that take place prior to marriage.

4. Publicly acknowledging one's homosexuality is called ____________________ ____________________.

5. Lesbians who want to create a separate women's culture distinct from heterosexuals and gay men are called lesbian ____________________.

6. The term used to describe a succession of marriages is ____________________ ____________________.

7. The greatest determinant of an aged person's sexual activity is the availability of a partner and ____________________.

8. Same-sex experience for heterosexuals in situations in which they are isolated from the other sex is ____________________ homosexuality.

9. Married partners who may mutually agree to allow sexual relationships with others have what is called an ____________________ ____________________.

10. Those who believe they can love and enjoy sex with both men and women are called ____________________.

bisexuals	separatists
coming out	serial monogamy
health	sex
nonmarital	love
open marriage	situational
premarital	

Essay

1. Cite two factors that have influenced attitudes thereby making premarital intercourse more acceptable.

2. It is a fact that young adults are getting married at a later age. Name and discuss three outcomes of this dramatic shift.

3. Living together has become more widespread and acceptable. Cite two advantages and two disadvantages to cohabitating.

4. Discuss two ways in which sexuality within marriage is different from premarital sex.

5. Aside from a decrease in the frequency of intercourse, list three sexual changes that aging women and three sexual changes aging men may face.

ANSWERS TO PRACTICE TEST QUESTIONS

Multiple Choice

1. d
2. c
3. a
4. b
5. a
6. d
7. a
8. b
9. c
10. b
11. a
12. b
13. a
14. d

True/False

1. F
2. T
3. F
4. F
5. T
6. T
7. F
8. T
9. F
10. F

Fill-In

1. sex/love
2. nonmarital
3. premarital sex
4. coming out
5. separatists
6. serial monogamy
7. health
8. situational
9. open marriage
10. bisexuals

Essay

1. Pages 232–234
2. Page 240
3. Pages 249–250
4. Page 255
5. Pages 265–266

OBSERVATIONS AND REFLECTIONS

OBSERVATION

Learning about Alternate Lifestyles

For many, the gay and lesbian community is an enigma; who are they? What do they do, talk about, and experience in their spare time? If you have ever wondered about this or if you feel as though you have not had exposure to gay men and lesbians, then you might consider taking this opportunity to become exposed—on their turf. If, however, you feel hostile or terribly uncomfortable about this activity, *do not* choose it.

Below are listed a number of places where gays and lesbians may go. They include bookstores, coffee houses, restaurants, bars, community centers, gay or lesbian support groups, and/or a university task force. To find specific addresses, you may wish to call the gay and lesbian community service center in your local area. After spending some time at any one of these places, ask yourself the following questions:

- Gay men and lesbians are . . . .

- I was surprised to find out . . . .

- As a result of visiting ____________________, I learned . . . .

- My attitude about the gay subculture is . . . .

OBSERVATION

Dating Customs

Dating is a relatively new phenomenon that is practiced mainly in Western countries. Observers of dating have noticed continual changes in these practices, as well as differences that exist across social classes and racial and ethnic groups.

Interview at least one or two acquaintances (preferably from another generation and/or social class and/or racial or ethnic group) to see how others regard this practice. Compare their experiences and attitudes to your own. Feel free to add or delete any questions you desire.

1. At what age did you begin to date?

2. How did you first meet this person?

3. Why did you desire to date this person?

4. What did you do on your first date?

5. What other people accompanied you?

6. Were any guidelines given to you by your parents or partner's parents?

7. Who picked up whom? Who selected the site of the date? Who drove? Who paid for the date?

8. Were there any physical intimacies made/exchanged during the date?

9. How did your first date conclude?

As a result of these interviews what did you learn? How did others' experiences and attitudes about dating differ from your own?

Adapted from Maxine Baca Zinn and D. Stanley Eitzin, *Diversity in Families,* 2d ed. (New York: Harper & Row, 1990).

REFLECTION

Women, Men, Sex, and Love

Women give sex to get love;
Men give love to get sex.

What are your feelings about this statement? How do your experiences compare with your feelings? Try rewriting the quote to reflect the way you perceive gender and sex are associated.

REFLECTION

Attitudes Toward Aging and Sex

Please respond to the following statements:

1. Older people are sexual people.

2. Most older women and men enjoy intercourse and/or masturbation.

3. Menopause is normal and natural and does not necessarily interfere with the expression of a woman's sexuality.

4. Nursing homes and residential care facilities should respect the privacy of older adults who wish to express their sexuality.

Look at your responses. Are your attitudes about sexuality and the aged accepting or not? How do you think your attitudes about the aging will impact your behavior when you are aged?

REFLECTION

Placing Relationships into Life's Continuum

Below is a continuum. On the far left is your birth (day 1) and on the far right is the number of years you believe you might live.

Day 1 **Age at Death**

|——|

Take some time to explore the significant life events that you anticipate. At what age do you expect each to occur? Fill out the continuum by drawing a small line relative to where you believe certain events will occur and briefly describe them. These can include:

- Graduated from high school
- Graduate from college
- Cite all the degrees you anticipate earning at the age you will obtain them
- First career job; retirement from that job
- Second or third career
- Marriage or significant relationship(s)
- Children; how many and how far apart
- Hobbies and travel
- Other

Now look at the whole continuum. Where are most events clustered? What do you have listed at the last one-third of your continuum? How do you feel about this time of your life? What are you doing now to plan for that time?

Think about your relationship and partner. Do you see yourself as being committed in a long-term relationship? Can you imagine yourself being sexual throughout your life? What attitudes do you have or can you begin to cultivate now to better prepare you for your later years as a sexual person?

GENDER AND SEXUAL IDENTITY QUESTIONS

Though a variety of issues are presented in this chapter, for the purposes of the gender paper, we will only focus on two of them: divorce and sexual orientation. If you feel a statement does not apply to you, then skip it and go onto the next.

Regarding Divorce

- I have/have not experienced divorce. (Include yourself if your parents are divorced.)

- This took place when I was _______ years old. It involved __________ and __________ (put in parties involved in the divorce).

- I recall feeling . . . .

- I believe this divorce has affected me . . . .

- As a result of this divorce, I have learned . . . .

(Repeat this activity if you have experienced more than one divorce.)

Regarding Sexual Orientation

- My sexual orientation is __________ and as a result of this I feel . . . .

- My sexual orientation became apparent to me when I was approximately ________ years old. This was a result of . . . .

- I recall having same-sex play with __________ when I was ________ years old. I remember feeling . . . .

(Repeat this if you recall experiencing this with additional people.)

- Regarding these experiences I now feel . . . .

- If my brother or sister confided in me that they were gay or lesbian, I would probably feel . . . . and tell them . . . .

I thought I had "escaped" the scars and trauma of my parents' divorce and considered myself lucky they had divorced when I was so young. In retrospect I have learned that the divorce did have a great impact on the development of my sexual identity. Not having a father take an active role in my life gave me a feeling of rejection I did not understand until just recently. I realized that I have developed many close personal friendships with the young men with whom I associate. I am reassured by their friendship and trust that I am appreciated by men even though I felt rejection from my father. —25-year-old Caucasian female student whose parents divorced when she was two

In junior high, I found myself still very curious about other boys and what they were like. I found myself attracted to some of them, but rationalized that it was a phase, and I was just curious and wanted to see what their bodies looked like. I kept telling myself that I was just a late bloomer and that I would start liking girls soon. I found that I was telling myself this throughout my entire four years in high school. Any day I would find the girl who would catch my attention (the truth was that I was still looking at other guys but hoping against hope that this was still a phase, albeit a long one). —24-year-old Caucasian gay male

When I was around six or seven, I was still curious about other children's bodies and how they looked. One day a friend and I were in my bedroom, and I recall that we pulled our pants down to play "doctor." His mother came into the room and caught us. She acted shocked and told us to put our clothes on "right now—that's nasty!!" "It's nasty" stuck in my mind for a long time. —20-year-old Caucasian male

CHAPTER 8
LOVE, INTIMACY, AND SEX

CHAPTER OUTLINE

Love and Sexuality
- Men, Sex, and Love
- Women, Sex, and Love
- Gay Men, Lesbians, and Love
- Sex Without Love

This Thing Called Love: The Phenomena of Love, Sex, and Commitment
- Prototypes of Love, Sex, and Commitment
- Attitudes and Behaviors Associated with Love

How Do I Love Thee? Approaches to the Study of Love
- Styles of Love
- *Self-Assessment: Your Style of Love*
- Romantic Love and Adrenaline: The Two Component Theory
- The Triangular Theory of Love
- Love as Attachment

Jealousy
- Jealousy in Cross-Cultural Perspective
- What Is Jealousy?
- Gender and Orientation Differences
- Managing Jealousy

The Transformation of Love: From Passion to Intimacy
- The Instability of Passionate Love
- Intimate Love: Commitment, Caring, and Self-Disclosure
- *Perspective 1: Making Love Last: The Role of Commitment*

LEARNING OBJECTIVES

At the conclusion of Chapter 8, students should be able to:

1. Discuss similarities and differences in attitudes toward love of heterosexual men and women and of gay men and lesbians.
2. Describe the prototypes of love, sex, and commitment and the similarities and differences between prototypes.
3. Identify the attitudes and behaviors associated with love.
4. List, describe, and give examples of the different styles of love.
5. Describe the two-component theory as applied to love.
6. List the components of the triangular theory of love and describe how they combine to create different forms of love.
7. Discuss love as a form of attachment, including the different styles of attachment.
8. Discuss jealousy, especially cross-cultural and psychological dimensions, types of jealousy, and jealousy as a boundary marker.
9. Describe gender and orientation differences in jealousy.
10. Discuss the role of commitment, caring, and self-disclosure in intimate love.

PRACTICE TEST QUESTIONS

Multiple Choice

1. Love is:
   a. a feeling
   b. constant and never changing
   c. an activity
   d. a and c only
2. Men are *more likely* than women to:
   a. separate sex and love
   b. find sex and love incompatible
   c. prefer sexual experiences that take place in a relational context
   d. experience jealousy over intimacy issues
3. Women:
   a. are more likely to report feelings of love if they are sexually involved with their partners
   b. report that love is closely related to feelings of self-esteem
   c. generally view sex from a relational perspective
   d. all of the above
4. Some researchers believe that the critical element that distinguishes being gay or lesbian from being heterosexual is:
   a. having sex with someone of the same sex
   b. the ability to personally acknowledge their sexual orientation
   c. the ability to love someone of the same sex
   d. the ability to publicly acknowledge their sexual orientation
5. The type of love that usually begins as friendship and gradually deepens into love is called:
   a. mania
   b. ludis
   c. storge
   d. agape
6. If we can understand jealousy we can:
   a. eliminate some of its pain
   b. see when and how it is functional and when it is not
   c. recognize its link with violence
   d. all of the above
7. The potential for jealousy is increased when there is a perceived lack of:
   a. independence
   b. self-esteem
   c. humor
   d. a and b only
8. The most intense kind of jealousy is:
   a. suspicious jealousy
   b. manic jealousy
   c. reactive jealousy
   d. depressive jealousy
9. Men tend to react to jealousy:
   a. with depression
   b. with confusion and mixed emotions
   c. by expressing anger
   d. all of the above

10. According to research done by Sternberg, time effects our level(s) of:
    a. intimacy
    b. passion
    c. commitment
    d. all of the above

11. The kind of love that is most likely to sustain over a period of time is:
    a. intimate love
    b. passionate love
    c. romantic love
    d. complex love

12. The determination to continue a relationship or marriage in the face of bad times as well as good is termed:
    a. intimate love
    b. commitment
    c. self-disclosing love
    d. caring

13. Models of how people define love, sex, and commitment are called:
    a. prototypes
    b. morals
    c. attachments
    d. values

14. Over time, romantic love tends to:
    a. increase
    b. stay the same
    c. end or be replaced by intimate love
    d. end or be replaced by passionate love

15. Intimate love is based on:
    a. commitment
    b. caring
    c. self-disclosure
    d. all of the above

Fill-In

1. Studies consistently demonstrate that for the majority of men, sex and love <u>can/cannot</u> (circle one) be easily separated.

2. Love relationships between homosexual couples are <u>equally/less</u> (circle one) satisfying than those of heterosexual couples.

3. The determination to continue in a relationship, reflecting stability, obligations, and social pressure, is better known as ____________________.

4. The type of love that idealizes its object, is marked by a high degree of physical and emotional arousal, and tends to be obsessive and all-consuming is known as ____________________.

5. The type of love that combines intimacy and passion, begins with friendship that intensifies with passion, and may or may not include commitment is ____________________.

6. The newest approach to the study of love that involves a close, enduring emotional bond that finds its roots in infancy is called ____________________.

7. The type of jealousy that occurs when a partner reveals a current, past, or anticipated relationship with another person is called ____________________.

8. Intensity of feeling does/does not (circle one) measure the depth of love.

9. Making another's needs as important as your own is called ____________________.

10. An aversive response caused by a partner's real, imagined, or likely involvement with a third person is called ____________________.

attachment	jealousy
caring	reactive
commitment	romantic love
infatuation	

Matching

Match the description with the style of love, as described by the sociologist John Lee:

1. Eros ________	a. companionate love
2. Mania _______	b. altruistic love
3. Ludis _______	c. love of beauty
4. Storge ______	d. practical love
5. Agape _______	e. playful love
6. Pragma ______	f. obsessive love

Essay

1. List and briefly discuss the three prototypes or attributes of sex. Which of the three is most important? Why?

2. Select either the two- or three-component theory of love and discuss how it explains the various aspects of love. Which theory, in your opinion, most accurately describes love?

3. Describe the effects that sexual orientation has on jealousy.

4. Identify and discuss two keys to making love last.

ANSWERS TO PRACTICE TEST QUESTIONS

Multiple Choice

1. d
2. a
3. d
4. c
5. c
6. d
7. d
8. c
9. c
10. d
11. a
12. b
13. a
14. c
15. d

Fill-In

1. can
2. equally
3. commitment
4. infatuation
5. romantic love
6. attachment
7. reactive
8. does not
9. caring
10. jealousy

Matching

1. c
2. f
3. e
4. a
5. b
6. d

Essay

1. Pages 278–280
2. Pages 286–289
3. Pages 298–299
4. Pages 302–304

OBSERVATIONS AND REFLECTIONS

OBSERVATION

Looking at Cohabitation

Does "living together" or cohabiting prior to marriage increase the success and improve the quality of a marriage? Not according to Elizabeth Thomson's and Ugo Colella's investigation of 13,000 adults sampled as part of the 1987–1988 National Survey of Families and Households. Generally, the couples who had cohabitated prior to marriage reported lower-quality marriages, less commitment to the institution of marriage, and a greater likelihood of divorce. Thomson and Colella found that the length of cohabitation increased these effects.

How do Thomson's and Colella's results compare with those that you gather? To find out, interview several couples and/or divorced individuals, some of whom cohabitated prior to marriage and some of whom did not. Ask them the following questions:

1. Did you cohabitate before getting married?

2. How long did you live together before you got married?

3. What prompted you to get married?

4. How would you rate the quality of your marriage?

5. Do you feel that living together increased or decreased or had no effect on the quality of your marriage?

6. Would you recommend living together?

7. Brainstorm the advantages and disadvantages of living together before marriage. Based on this list and your feelings about the subject, which lifestyle (living together before marriage or not) would you choose?

Source: Elizabeth Thomson and Ugo Colella, "Cohabitation and Marital Stability: Quality or Commitment?" *Journal of Marriage and the Family* 54 (May 1992): 259–267.

OBSERVATION

Look on the Radio

Turn on your radio, find a channel that has songs (with lyrics) that suit your style and, for the next half hour or so, *listen* to what messages love songs give about sex and love. What kinds of love are sung about? Romantic? Companionate? What messages are given and what kinds of visual images accompany them?

OBSERVATION

Looking at Love

Interview one or two persons who you know is/are in a long-term (at least two years), committed relationship. Ask them how they knew when they were "in love." Find out if their level of intimacy has changed over time. Ask them the differences between being "in love" versus being "in infatuation" with another. Ask them what qualities contribute to a successful relationship.

REFLECTION

Vows and Prenuptial Agreements

1. There are some who feel that a "prenuptial agreement" or contract is an important component to consider before marriage. Assuming you were one of these individuals, what might you include in yours? In addition to material belongings, you might also consider including a division of household tasks, babysitting arrangements, career decisions, pets, as well as agreements about relations with in-laws and friends and discussions about religion.

2. This activity is done best when you have 15 or 20 minutes alone to reflect on what your marriage means to you. Compose your marriage vows. This should be an accurate reflection of how you perceive your marriage to be. Hold onto this list and reflect back upon it from time to time. If you are married, how close does your marriage come from meeting these vows? Why or why not?

What did you learn about your expectations of marriage from this exercise?

REFLECTION

Basic Styles of Love

The sociologist John Lee describes six basic styles of love and provides brief descriptions of each type. Which type(s) of love have you experienced? With whom? Which type have you found the most satisfying? Why?

REFLECTION

Your Love Triangle

The textbook discusses the triangular theory of love by Robert Sternberg. Using the diagrams in Figure 8 as a guide, think about a relationship you have been in, or one you know well, and draw the triangle to represent the Intimacy, Passion, and Commitment levels. Draw one triangle for each partner. If you are in a relationship, you might explain this concept to your partner and ask them to draw a triangle representing how they see these three elements in your relationship.

Are the triangles representing each person's level of these elements similar, or are there differences?

Reflecting on this, does it give some insight into the weaknesses or strengths of the relationship?

Are there any ways to help these three important aspects of your relationship become stronger?

Keep these diagrams to come back to in several months to see if there are changes you notice in the relationship.

GENDER AND SEXUAL IDENTITY QUESTIONS

- I have/have not been in love.

- The most profound type of love I ever experienced was with __________. I found it to be . . . .

- As a result of this I learned . . . .

- The most satisfying type of love for me is __________ because . . . .

- Probably the most painful experience I have had as a result of love involved . . . .

- I experienced or observed jealousy when . . . .

- My experience of love has affected my sexual identity by . . . .

During my early teen years, my budding sexuality was motivated by rebellion against my grandmother, her emotional abuse, and denial of sexuality as a normal and healthy expression of one's identity. My rebellion took the form of sexual promiscuity by the time I had become 14 years old. Sex became a means of both defying my grandmother and obtaining love and closeness, if only for a little while. —39-year-old female Caucasian

People would perceive me as self-assured, independent, confident, and secure, and in many areas I am all of those things. That doesn't mean a lot though, if you can't be free to love and be loved. —27-year-old female Caucasian

I was away from home for the very first time and got caught up in the college scene. I had my very first sexual experience in my first year of college on my eighteenth birthday. It was with someone I had just met that night at a party. I knew very well what I wanted to do that night. I was getting tired of being sexually naive except for information I got from other people's experiences. I was very disappointed after that experience because I did not have fun, and I never really saw that guy again. There was no emotion. After that experience, I thought every sexual experience was supposed to be uncomfortable. I felt I had to give in to the guy's passes and have sex with him the very first night or within the first few weeks. Thank goodness it did not take very many experiences like that to knock some sense into me about what a relationship should be. When I realized that a relationship need not be emotionless and uncaring, I stopped all sexual activity until I was sure that I was interested in the person beyond just one night. —26-year-old Caucasian female

CHAPTER 9
COMMUNICATING ABOUT SEX

CHAPTER OUTLINE

LEARNING OBJECTIVES

At the conclusion of Chapter 9, students should be able to:

1. Describe the characteristics of communication, including transaction, process, and symbolic.
2. Discuss the cultural, social, and psychological contexts of communication with examples of each.
3. Identify and give examples of the functions of nonverbal communication and of the role of proximity, eye contact, and touching.
4. Describe communication in beginning and established relationships, including the halo effect, interest and opening lines, the first move, initiating and directing sexual activity, and gay and lesbian relationships.
5. List and give examples of communication patterns in satisfied relationships and discuss gender differences in marital communication.
6. Discuss the obstacles and problems with sexual vocabulary in talking about sex.
7. Describe and give examples of the keys to good sexual communication, including self-disclosure, trust, and feedback.
8. List the guidelines for effective feedback with examples of each.
9. Discuss types of conflicts and the nature and sources of power in intimate relationships, including the power of love.
10. Describe sexual conflicts, including sex and power issues, the characteristics of conflict resolution in happy and unhappy couples, and strategies for resolving conflicts.

PRACTICE TEST QUESTIONS

Multiple Choice

1. Two types of communication problems that occur in relationships are:
   a. failure to self-disclose and poor communication skills
   b. lack of commitment and low self-esteem
   c. lack of eye contact and unexpressive body language
   d. blaming others and talking too much

2. Whether individuals have equal or unequal power status in a relationship profoundly affects:
   a. the quantity of sexual activity
   b. society at large
   c. communication
   d. none of the above are affected

3. When we consider gender role and sexual orientation we find that:
   a. lesbian relationships are likely to be most communicative
   b. heterosexual relationships are moderately communicative
   c. gay relationships are less communicative
   d. all of the above are true

4. Which of the following are more likely to find it difficult to discuss sex because it arouses anxiety or feelings of guilt?
   a. erotophilics
   b. erotophobics
   c. sexually inexperienced people
   d. most people

5. Touch:
   a. often signals intimacy, immediacy, and emotional closeness
   b. is initiated by men equally as often as by women
   c. appears to be linked to self-disclosure
   d. all of the above

6. In new or developing relationships, communication about sexuality is generally:
   a. direct and straightforward
   b. indirect and ambiguous
   c. non-existent

7. A major reason why lesbians may have sex less often than other kinds of couples is:
   a. they are inherently less sexual than others
   b. many lesbians are not comfortable in the role of sexual aggressor
   c. they are often unsure of another's sexual orientation
   d. that many lesbians experience a lack of self-worth

8. In established relationships between men and women, many women feel more comfortable with overtly initiating sex because:
   a. of the decreasing significance of the double standard
   b. it may be viewed as an expression of love
   c. it can be the result of couples becoming more egalitarian in their gender-role attitudes
   d. all of the above

9. One of the key differences between heterosexual couples and gay couples is:
   a. how they handle extrarelational sex
   b. their enjoyment of sex
   c. who initiates sex
   d. the type of communication that is expressed prior to having sex

10. Which of the following is/are true regarding marital communication?
    a. wives send clearer messages to their husbands than their husbands send to them
    b. husbands, more than wives, tend to give neutral messages
    c. wives tends to set the emotional tone of an argument
    d. all of the above

11. Probably the most negative effect on intimacy is due to:
    a. a lack of sex
    b. power imbalances or the blatant use of power
    c. differences in financial status between partners
    d. differences in education

Fill-In

1. The thread that connects sexuality and intimacy is ____________________.

2. When we communicate, we use ____________________, such as words or gestures, that stand for something else.

3. For a message to be most effective, both the verbal and nonverbal components must be in ____________________.

4. Nearness in physical space and time, feeling "distinct" or "close" in a relationship is called ____________________.

5. The assumption that attractive people possess more desirable social characteristics than unattractive people is otherwise known as the ____________________ ____________________.

6. Sexual initiations are more often/less often (circle one) successful in marital relationships than in new or dating relationships.

7. Studies suggest that poor communication skills precede/follow (circle one) marital problems.

8. The belief in the reliability and integrity of a person is known as ____________________.

9. The communication process in which people perceive interference from others in achieving their goals is otherwise known as ____________________.

10. The more intimate two people become, the more/less (circle one) likely they may be to experience conflict.

11. ____________________ is the ability or potential ability to influence another person or group.

12. The theory which explains power in terms of involvement and needs in a relationship is called ____________________ ____________________ and ____________________ theory.

agreement	proximity
communication	relative love
conflict	need
halo effect	symbols
power	trust

True/False

Mark T or F on the line before the question.

____ 1. The quality of the communication between two people affects the quality of their relationship.

____ 2. Despite stereotypes of women touching and men avoiding touch, studies suggest that there are no consistent differences between the sexes in the amount of overall touching.

____ 3. Little or no value is placed on physical attractiveness during the initial meeting and early stages of a relationship.

____ 4. The majority of people begin their sexual involvement in the context of an ongoing relationship.

____ 5. Because so much of our sexual communication is direct, unambiguous, and verbal, there is little risk of misinterpretation between men and women.

____ 6. Within established relationships, men continue to overtly initiate sexual encounters more frequently than women.

____ 7. Researchers have found that men and women in satisfied relationships are willing to engage in conflict in nondestructive ways.

____ 8. The process of articulating our feelings about sex are usually quite easy because of the positive models that most children have grown up with.

____ 9. One of the keys to good communication is to avoid self-disclosure because it creates an environment of misunderstanding.

____ 10. The most crucial variable in explaining the power structure of a relationship is the degree to which one spouse loves and needs the other.

Essay

1. The three concepts used to describe the nature of communication are transaction, process, and symbols. Briefly discuss each concept as it relates to communication in relationships.

2. Describe the functions of conveying interpersonal attitudes, expressing emotions, and handling the ongoing interaction in close relationships.

3. Discuss three reasons why misinterpretation of sexual communication can occur between women and men.

4. What are the three keys to good communication and how are they involved in promoting open, honest communication about sex?

5. List and discuss two strategies for resolving conflicts within relationships.

ANSWERS TO PRACTICE TEST QUESTIONS

Multiple Choice

1. d
2. c
3. d
4. b
5. d
6. b
7. b
8. d
9. a
10. d
11. b

Fill-In

1. communication
2. symbols
3. agreement
4. proximity
5. halo effect
6. more often
7. precede
8. trust
9. conflict
10. more
11. Power
12. relative love/need

True/False

1. T
2. T
3. F
4. T
5. F
6. T
7. T
8. F
9. F
10. T

Essay

1. Pages 309–310
2. Page 315
3. Pages 323–324
4. Pages 332–334
5. Pages 343–344

OBSERVATIONS AND REFLECTIONS

OBSERVATION

Games Singles Play

The purpose of this activity is to observe people communicating in a setting in which they feel comfortable. Single people were chosen because you can observe a wide range of both verbal and nonverbal communication in their desire to get to know one another. A setting that you may choose to visit should involve or cater to single people, such as a bar, community event (watch newspaper ads), or apartment complex.

While at the site, take a seat away from people and watch their body language. What gestures are used to communicate? How close do people sit next to one another? Can you differentiate those whose relationship is established from those who are newly acquainted? Observe the level of eye contact, posing, and touching that occurs. Who appears to be the more aggressive? What else do you notice about body language that helps to communicate interest or desire?

REFLECTION

Language and Sexuality

There are many reasons why people are uncomfortable talking about sex. Some of these include personal anxieties and cultural factors. Another reason that people are uncomfortable is that they don't have a "language" they feel comfortable using to discuss sexual issues and feelings. Paul Cashman, Ph.D., has suggested that we have four "language systems" to use when we talk about sexuality. They are:

1. *Child language.* These are the words used by our parents when we were very young—often related to toilet training. Words like *wienie, bottom, tushy, ticket, pee-pee,* and *poo-poo* are examples of these types of words.
2. *Slang or street language.* This category probably has the greatest number of words. Often this is the way we talk about sex with our peers, and these are the words we see in graffiti in bathrooms. Words like cock and cunt are examples of street language.
3. *Euphemisms.* These are the words that allow us to talk about sex in "polite" conversations and relate to our Victorian heritage. Words like *making love, that time of month,* and *in the family way* are examples of euphemisms.
4. *Medical-scientific language.* From school, books, and others we learn that there is a technical language often used by professionals or parents to talk about sexuality. Words like *intercourse, coitus interruptus, penis,* and *menstruation* are examples of this type of language.

For each category write down some of the words that you have used or might use to talk about sex:

CHILD-LANGUAGE

SLANG OR STREET LANGUAGE

EUPHEMISMS

MEDICAL-SCIENTIFIC LANGUAGE

After doing the exercise answer these questions:

For which category was it easy to list words?

For which groups was it hardest to think of words?

Which words do you think would be recognized by most others and which are limited to family or a particular culture?

Which types of words are you most comfortable with?

Each of us needs to think about what type of language we are comfortable using in different situations. There is nothing wrong with using child language in your intimate relationships, or street language if you or your partner are comfortable with it and find it exciting. What is important is finding words and ways to discuss sexual issues in a comfortable way. Whereas a great deal of sexual communication is non-verbal, the more words we have, the more precise and accurate we can be in communicating with others.

Note: The article cited is from SEICUS Reports, September 1980.

REFLECTION

Friendships and the Role of Communication

Take a moment to recall a person with whom you have/have had your closest friendship/relationship. What made this friendship special? How long did you share this bond? Now try to recall the communication patterns you shared with this person. Did you exchange secrets with each other? What was it about your ability to communicate with this person that made him or her so special? Was he or she non-judgmental? A good listener? Expressive? Comfortable with quiet times? Revealing? Able to acknowledge your feelings? Able to disagree freely? What other ways did you share your feelings with one another?

Now think about the communication patterns you have with other friends. What ways do you demonstrate your feelings? Do you desire a more in-depth relationship with anyone? If so, how might you expand the way you communicate in order to nurture this relationship?

PERSONAL INVOLVEMENT ASSESSMENT

The Closer You Get, the Faster I Run

Ira Wolfman writes of something to which many people can relate: fear of intimacy. In fact, he never leaves home without his "Intimacy Allergy" card. He's a self-admitted "Get close—get away!" guy who has many feelings emerge when faced with intimacy in relationships—for example, nervousness, fear, anger, and craziness. Even though he considers himself to be warm, affectionate, intelligent, and caring, if faced with the possibility that a relationship will become close, he forgets these characteristics when he starts thinking of "marr...—you know, the m-word."

Mr. Wolfman, in speaking with Elaine Hatfield of the University of Hawaii at Manoa, learned that his fears of intimacy matched many of the findings of Professor Hatfield's research and that his fears are shared by many—by women perhaps only slightly less than by men.

What fears do you have about intimacy in relationships? Think about any fears you have about getting close, being intimate. Write down five of them. If you do not have any such fears, write down ones you believe are frequently felt by others you know.

1.

2.

3.

4.

5.

Now, read over the six fears that Mr. Wolfman described.

1. Loving means risking hurt, risking loss, risking abandonment.
2. Oh, God! You'll find out who I really am!
3. Making choices means forsaking choices.
4. You're going to use it against me, aren't you?
5. You'll smother me . . . and I'll hate it.
6. You'll smother me . . . and I'll love it.

Next, write how you relate to these fears.

According to Hatfield, both men and women need to combine the classically feminine need for connection with the classically male need for independence. Presently, therapists utilize various techniques in teaching couples how to achieve greater intimacy, including (1) encouraging people to accept themselves as they are, to recognize their intimates for what they are . . . and let them be, and to express themselves, and (2) teaching people to deal with their intimate's reactions. But Dr. Hatfield cautions: "As long as men were fleeing from intimacy, women could safely pursue them. Now that men are turning around to face them, women may well find themselves taking flight."

Source: Ira Wolfman, "The Closer You Get, the Faster I Run." *Ms.,* September 1985, 934–935, 112.

GENDER AND SEXUAL IDENTITY QUESTIONS

Though you have to a degree already revealed how friends, family, and other significant people and events had an impact on your sexual being, you haven't yet been asked to specifically address communication patterns as they relate to the above. You are aware by now that the quality of the communication affects the quality of the relationship.

Take a few minutes to reflect on the quality of your own communication patterns and history by completing the following statements.

- When very young my communication with my parents was . . . .

- As I grew older, communication with my parents became . . . . because . . . .

- As a result of this I felt . . . .

- I observed my parents' communication to be . . . .

- I believe this affected me . . . .

- When it comes to trust, I . . . .

- When I think about self-disclosure or revealing myself to another, I . . . .

- When close friends disclose facts about themselves to me, my feedback is often . . . .

- When conflict occurs with others, I . . . .

- My greatest strength as a communicator is my ability to . . . .

- My greatest weakness as a communicator is . . . .

- As far as communication goes, my greatest desire would be to . . . .

I learned through my parents that sex is not a "dirty" thing. It is the most incredibly wonderful experience that two loving people can share together. It is because of my mom and dad that I believe so strongly in the good that sex can bring to an already close and loving relationship. —24-year-old Caucasian male

Their regular fights and heated arguments, though never physically abusive, were often cruel and verbally offensive. I remember many times the issue of sex being thrown into the arguments only to be used against or to hurt the other person. Too many nights my mom slept downstairs on the couch. They clearly lacked healthy communication. To me this was not an example of a trusting or loving relationship. While I realize it was their mistakes, it makes me worry about what my relations will become. —25-year-old male Caucasian looking back at his parents' relationship

CHAPTER 10
SEXUAL EXPRESSION

CHAPTER OUTLINE

LEARNING OBJECTIVES

At the conclusion of Chapter 10, students should be able to:

1. Describe the elements of sexual attractiveness along gender and orientation lines and discuss the impact of the halo effect.
2. Discuss sexual desire, including its nature and erotophilia/erotophobia.
3. Explain sexual scripts, including cultural, interpersonal, and intrapersonal scripts with examples of each.
4. Describe the role and function of autoeroticism, including sexual fantasies, dreams, and masturbation through the life cycle.
5. Identify various types of sensuous touching and their role in sexuality.
6. Describe the various meanings associated with kissing and its role as a form of sexual behavior.
7. Discuss oral-genital sex, including cunnilingus and fellatio, changing attitudes toward it, and varying incidence by ethnicity.
8. Discuss the incidence, meanings, and types of sexual intercourse.
9. Discuss anal eroticism, varying incidence by sexual orientation and ethnicity, and health concerns.

PRACTICE TEST QUESTIONS

Multiple Choice

1. Men and women who accept and enjoy their sexuality, seek out sexual situations, and engage in more autoerotic and interpersonal sexual situations are said to be:
   a. erotophobic
   b. erotophilic
   c. heteroerotic
   d. sexual perverts
2. When sexual scripts enable people to give meaning to their physiological responses, the meaning of which depends on the situation, it is referred to as a/an:
   a. cultural component
   b. interpersonal component
   c. intrapersonal component
   d. anatomical component
3. Fantasies:
   a. radically alter through adulthood
   b. serve no function in maintaining our psychic equilibrium
   c. have distinct differences depending on the gender
   d. are dangerous because they are accurate indicators of what sexual activities a person is likely to engage in
4. Through masturbation, children and adolescents learn:
   a. more about their bodies and what is sexually pleasing
   b. that there are harmful physical effects associated with this activity
   c. to simulate sexual intercourse
   d. nothing about themselves
5. When adults find their child masturbating they are most likely to:
   a. react overwhelmingly negatively by reprimanding their child
   b. calmly tell the child to go into another room
   c. see it as a positive outlet and expression of sexuality
   d. encourage him or her to masturbate even more
6. Touching:
   a. is a sign of caring and a signal for arousal
   b. is usually more significant for new couples than for those who have been together for a longer period of time
   c. in order to be effective, should be directed at the genitals or erogenous zones
   d. is straightforward and not subject to interpretation
7. The most acceptable of all premarital sexual activities is probably:
   a. touching and caressing
   b. kissing
   c. manual genital intercourse
   d. intercourse
8. Although criminal statutes against oral sex apply to men and women of all sexual orientations, in recent years sodomy laws have been enforced only against:
   a. minors or those under 21 years of age
   b. ethnic minorities
   c. gay men and lesbian women
   d. they are uniformly enforced

9. Because of HIV, the activity which is potentially the most dangerous is:
   a. cunnilingus or fellatio
   b. deep kissing
   c. penile/vaginal intercourse
   d. anal intercourse

10. The most universal of all sexual behaviors probably is/are:
   a. sexual fantasies
   b. intercourse
   c. fellatio and cunnilingus
   d. kissing

True/False

Mark T or F on the line before the question.

____ 1. Research has demonstrated that there is one universal standard for what is considered to be sexually attractive.

____ 2. Blumstein and Schwartz found that the happiest people in cohabitating and married relationships considered their partner to be attractive.

____ 3. Sexual desire is subject to considerable variations throughout one's lifetime.

____ 4. Many people fantasize about things that they would never actually do.

____ 5. Our gender roles have little or no impact on how we behave sexually.

____ 6. It is the guilt, rather than the fantasizing itself, that may be harmful to a relationship.

____ 7. Attitudes towards masturbation and masturbatory behavior do not vary between ethnic groups.

____ 8. Women who masturbate appear to hold more positive sexual attitudes and are more likely to be orgasmic than women who do not masturbate.

____ 9. The amount of kissing that occurs in a relationship appears to differ according to sexual orientation.

____ 10. Among gay men, anal intercourse is more common than oral sex.

Fill-In

1. Plans that organize and give direction to our behaviors and that strongly influence our sexual activities as men and women are called ____________________ ____________________.

2. Sexual activities that involve only the self, that include sexual fantasies, masturbation, and erotic dreams is referred to as ____________________.

3. In looking at a person's life span, we are capable of experiencing genital pleasure from ____________________ through ____________________.

4. As men grow older, the frequency of masturbation ____________________ while that of sexual intercourse ____________________.

5. Masters and Johnson suggest a form of touching they call ____________________.

6. Our earliest interpersonal sexual experience is usually ____________________.

7. Oral stimulation of a women's vulva is called ____________________.

8. Oral stimulation of a man's penis is called ____________________.

9. A term for the licking of the anal region is ____________________.

10. If the penis or a foreign object is inserted into the anus, it must be ____________________ before insertion into the vagina because it may cause vaginal infection.

analingus	declines
autoeroticism	kissing
birth/old age	pleasuring
cunnilingus	sexual scripts
fellatio	washed
increases	

Essay

1. Given the choice between the cultural, interpersonal, or intrapersonal components of sexual scripts, select one and discuss how it gives direction to our sexual activities.

2. Discuss two functions of sexual fantasy.

3. State three positive functions of masturbation.

4. Describe the forms that nongenital touching and caressing can take and two advantages of this type of pleasuring.

ANSWERS TO PRACTICE TEST QUESTIONS

Multiple Choice

1. b
2. c
3. c
4. a
5. a
6. a
7. b
8. c
9. d
10. a

True/False

1. F
2. T
3. T
4. T
5. F
6. T
7. F
8. T
9. T
10. F

Fill-In

1. sexual scripts
2. autoeroticism
3. birth/old age
4. increases/declines
5. pleasuring
6. kissing
7. cunnilingus
8. fellatio
9. analingus
10. washed

Essay

1. Pages 355–358
2. Pages 359–361
3. Page 365
4. Page 369–370

OBSERVATIONS AND REFLECTIONS

OBSERVATION

Let's Talk About S...E...X

Sex ranks with money and death as being one of the least honestly talked about subjects in our culture. If you are comfortable and with a trusted friend, interview him or her to assess their attitudes and beliefs regarding the behaviors listed below. Request honesty in the interview and provide respect and confidentiality.

What is/are your:

- preferences regarding sexual attractiveness?
- ways to initiate physical contact in courtship or marriage?
- attitudes about sexual fantasies and dreams?
- feelings about oral genital sex?
- thoughts about the importance of touch and caressing?
- preferences regarding sexual intercourse?
- feelings about anal eroticism and intercourse?

What did you learn as a result of this interview and discussion? How do your own thoughts, feelings, and attitudes compare with the person you interviewed? What was the most difficult question to ask? Why? What was the easiest question to ask? Why?

REFLECTION

Rating Sexual Attractiveness

Strong and DeVault, in their textbook, review and discuss literature that relates to sexual attractiveness. Acknowledging that different cultures, genders, and individuals view aspects of sexual attractiveness differently and uniquely, take a few minutes to think about what you find attractive in a potential partner. Consider emotional and psychological as well as physical factors. Organize your list in terms of the importance of each feature. Compare your list with that which is cited in the textbook. How does it compare? If you desire, share this activity and compare your list with a trusted friend's.

The physical qualities I find most desirable in a potential partner are:

Priority

______________________________ ________

______________________________ ________

______________________________ ________

______________________________ ________

______________________________ ________

______________________________ ________

The psychological or emotional qualities I find most desirable in a potential partner are:

Priority

______________________________ ________

______________________________ ________

______________________________ ________

______________________________ ________

______________________________ ________

______________________________ ________

As a result of this, I learned:

REFLECTION

Looking at Fantasyland

Nearly everyone has sexual fantasies; however, not everyone takes the time to write them down and, only if they are comfortable, share them with a companion.

Write down two or three of your favorite sexual fantasies. Remember, they are only for you, if you so desire.

Fantasy #1

Fantasy #2

How easy or difficult was it to re-create the sexual scenarios? How did they appear to you once you saw them in writing? Did you become re-aroused or did they lose their impact? If you shared them with a close friend, what was their reaction? How comfortable were you while sharing them?

You may choose to do this activity from time to time and observe the changes and common themes that take place over time.

REFLECTION

The Treasure Island Syndrome

Imagine yourself stranded on an island for one week with someone of the opposite sex, or same sex if you are gay or lesbian. Knowing that your time together would be limited to only one week, what characteristics would you desire in this person?

Now imagine that you are on that island for one year. What characteristics would you desire? List these characteristics from the one you desire most to the one that is least important.

How do these lists differ? How important are these characteristics in a long-term dating partner? How can you tell if your partner has these qualities? How far down the list would you go before letting go of the relationship? Which of the above-mentioned qualities do you possess?

If you are in a relationship and are willing to do so, ask your partner to participate in this same activity and then share and compare results.

GENDER AND SEXUAL IDENTITY QUESTIONS

Because this chapter addresses a number of sexual attitudes and behaviors that have been touched on in earlier gender questions, we choose to highlight only two aspects of gender identity—the cultural and religious ones. These dimensions are particularly relevant to those whose early development followed more traditional lines or whose families placed an emphasis in these areas.

Please respond to the following statements:

Concerning Culture

- The sexual behaviors that my culture approves and emphasizes are . . . .

- The sexual behaviors that my culture discourages or prohibits are . . . .

- In terms of what my culture has taught me about sexual behavior, I agree with . . . .

- In terms of what my culture has taught me about sexual behavior, I disagree with . . . .

- I handle the discrepancy between my culture's teachings and my own by . . . . (Do not complete if you do not feel a discrepancy.)

- In terms of what my culture has taught me about sexual behavior, I plan on passing down to my children . . . .

- In traveling, I have been exposed to another culture's view of sexuality and it has affected me by . . . .

Concerning Religion

- The sexual behaviors that my religion approves and emphasizes are . . . .

- The sexual behaviors that my religion discourages or prohibits are . . . .

- In terms of what my religion has taught me about sexual behavior, I agree with . . . .

- In terms of what my religion has taught me about sexual behavior, I disagree with . . . .

- I handle the discrepancy between my religion's teachings and my own by . . . . (Do not complete if you do not feel a discrepancy.)

- In terms of what my religion has taught me about sexual behavior, I plan on passing down to my children . . . .

The issue of cultural relationships is the most difficult aspect of my identity. After enrolling in a college speech class, I became more comfortable talking to the opposite sex and with expressing my views, a trait not found in many Nigerian households. My dad didn't approve of my friendships because he believes that the only time a woman should be involved with a man is if it is going to lead to marriage. On the subject of marriage, most Nigerians marry within their own culture. It's at this point in my life where both cultures clashed. —24-year-old female Nigerian-American

I am caught in the middle of two worlds. With this dilemma, I'm not able to find my self-identity, let alone my sexual identity. Am I a Vietnamese trapped within an American culture, or am I really an American trapped within a Vietnamese body? I'm torn apart by what is right in the American culture but might not be right in the Asian culture almost every single day. In her essay, entitled "To Be Or Not To Be," the author concluded that TO BE an American or NOT TO BE an American is one question. TO BE what people want her to be or NOT TO BE herself was the other question. —22-year-old Vietnamese woman from a family of 11 children

On the wedding night when a man discovered that his new wife was not a virgin, he returned her to her parents. "Poor parents, they were the talk of the town," my mother would tell me. —20-year-old Latina describes her mother's story that has scared her for years

Religion was always an important part of my family life, but it appears that it did not have that great of an impact on my early sexual identity. However, as I have gotten older and more specifically in the last few years, religion has once again come into my life and now plays a significant role in my attitudes towards sex. I try to follow the teachings, but this is extremely difficult for me now because I love sex so much. There always seems to be a constant battle going on inside my head of what is acceptable as compared to that which is not. —22-year-old male Caucasian

CHAPTER 11
ATYPICAL AND PARAPHILIC SEXUAL BEHAVIOR

CHAPTER OUTLINE

Atypical Versus Paraphilic Behavior
- *Perspective 1: The Myth of Sexual Addiction: Caveat Emptor II*

Atypical Sexual Behaviors
- Cross-Dressing
- *Perspective 2: Carnival: Sexual Transgression in Contemporary Brazil*
- Domination and Submission

The Paraphilias
- Studying Paraphilic Behavior
- Characteristics of Paraphiliacs
- The Development of Paraphilias

Noncoercive Paraphilias
- Fetishism
- Transvestism
- Zoophilia

Coercive Paraphilias
- Voyeurism
- Exhibitionism
- Telephone Scatalogia
- Frotteurism
- Necrophilia
- Pedophilia
- Sexual Sadism and Sexual Masochism

Treating Paraphiliacs
- Decreasing Paraphilic Behavior
- Teaching Social Skills

LEARNING OBJECTIVES

At the conclusion of Chapter 11, students should be able to:

1. Compare and contrast atypical and paraphilic sexual behavior.
2. Discuss cross-dressing in popular and gay culture and as a form of "gender relaxation."
3. Discuss domination and submission as atypical behavior, including bondage, the D/S subculture, and D/S as "theater."
4. Describe briefly the characteristics of paraphiliacs.
5. List and describe the factors in the development and maintenance of paraphiliacs.
6. Describe and characterize the noncoercive paraphilias, including fetishism, transvestism, and zoophilia.
7. Describe and characterize the coercive paraphilias, including voyeurism, exhibitionism, telephone scatologia and frotteurism, and necrophilia.
8. Describe pedophilia, including types of pedophiles, cross-sex and same sex pedophilia, and female pedophilia.
9. Discuss sexual sadism and sexual masochism, including autoerotic asphyxia.
10. Describe the treatment of paraphiliacs, including decreasing paraphilic behavior and teaching social skills.

PRACTICE TEST QUESTIONS

Multiple Choice

1. Sexual behaviors that are classified as mental disorders are known as:
   a. atypical sexual behaviors
   b. abnormal sexual behaviors
   c. paraphilias
   d. none of the above
2. Which statement about cross-dressing is *false*?
   a. At times in history cross-dressing has been celebrated.
   b. At times in history cross-dressing has been condemned.
   c. All cross-dressers are transvestites.
   d. In structured occasions such as all-male retreats, cross-dressing is seen as a form of male bonding.
3. The critical element in domination and submission is:
   a. pain
   b. power
   c. whips
   d. intimacy
4. Which of these is NOT a form of domination and submission?
   a. bondage and discipline
   b. humiliation
   c. kennelism
   d. stabbing
5. According to the authors, which of these is NOT a characteristic of paraphiliacs?
   a. they are most likely to be males ranging in age from 45–65
   b. a strong need to act out long-standing, unusual erotic sexual fantasies
   c. an inability to have a conventional sexual relationship
   d. they are most likely to be males ranging in age from 15–25
6. Which of these is/are a non-coercive paraphilia(s)?
   a. fetishism
   b. exhibitionism
   c. transvestism
   d. all of the above
7. What is the recommended clinical treatment for transvestites?
   a. Use aversion therapy.
   b. Use drug therapy.
   c. Use intense psychotherapy.
   d. Help the transvestite and those close to him accept his cross-dressing.
8. Zoophilia has been associated with:
   a. witchcraft
   b. worship of elephants and kangaroos
   c. wearing clothes made of animal skins
   d. living in zoos in Philadelphia
9. The difference between coercive paraphilias and non-coercive paraphilias is:
   a. the age of the youngest participant
   b. coercive paraphilias involve victimization and cause harm
   c. coercive paraphilias involve more than one other person
   d. men do coercive paraphilias and women do non-coercive paraphilias

10. All of the following are true of exhibitionism EXCEPT:
    a. it is a common paraphilia
    b. it often goes along with voyeurism and frotteurism
    c. those involved are usually men over 50
    d. those involved usually expose themselves to children, adolescents, and young women, but rarely to older women.

11. Young boys (12 or younger) having sexual contact with adult females:
    a. only rarely occurs
    b. has never been reported
    c. is fairly common
    d, is always regarded as negative by the boy

12. Treatments now used for paraphiliacs include all of the following EXCEPT:
    a. covert sensitization
    b. satiation
    c. signal punishment
    d. physical castration

True/False

Mark T or F on the line before the question.

____ 1. The terms *atypical sexual behaviors* and *abnormal sexual behaviors* describe the same thing.

____ 2. Atypical sexual behaviors are not rare.

____ 3. Paraphilias are much more likely to occur among gay men and bisexuals than among heterosexuals.

____ 4. Psychologists believe that fetishistic behavior may have its roots in childhood incidents.

____ 5. According to the authors, transvestites differ from cross-dressers in the compulsivity and sexual arousal associated with their behavior.

____ 6. All participants in necrophilia are psychotic and sadistic and suffer from mental impairment.

____ 7. If a heterosexually-identified man is a pedophile, he only molests girls.

____ 8. The distinction used to separate consensual sexual sadism and masochism from domination and submission is that in sadism and masochism the activities are extreme, compulsive, and dangerous.

____ 9. Teaching social skills and stress management can be important elements in working with the treatment of paraphilias.

____ 10. Sexual addiction is believed by most psychologists and researchers to be a paraphilia that should be recognized as a dysfunction by the American Psychological Association.

Fill-In

1. The negative term commonly used to describe abnormal or excessive sexual desire in a woman is

    ________________________.

2. The term ____________________ ________________ ____________________ is used to refer to sexual arousal derived from the consensual acting out of sexual scenes in which one person dominates and the other submits.

3. A woman specializing in "discipline" in sexual scenes is known as a ______________________.

4. The sexualization and fixation on inanimate objects is known as ______________________.

5. Sexual excitement derived from animals is known as bestiality or ______________________.

6. The name of the paraphilia where there is sexual rubbing against another person without their consent is ______________________.

7. Sexual excitement from secretly watching another person who is nude, disrobing, or engaging in sexual activity is known as ______________________.

8. The intense recurring urge to display one's genitals to an unsuspecting stranger is known as ______________________.

9. Recurrent intense sexual urges and sexually arousing fantasies involving sexual activity with children is called ______________________.

10. Strangulation or suffocation practiced during masturbation to heighten arousal by cutting off oxygen is called ______________________.

domination and submission	masturbatory asphyxia
dominatrix	nymphomania
exhibitionism	pedophilia
fetishism	voyeurism
frotteurism	zoophilia

Short Answer

1. Compare and contrast atypical and paraphilic sexual behavior.

2. List and describe four factors that help explain the development and maintenance of paraphilias in individuals.

3. What advice does the textbook give about how to deal with obscene phone calls?

4. Discuss the four approaches to treating paraphilias and the methods used with each of these approaches.

ANSWERS TO PRACTICE TEST QUESTIONS

Multiple Choice

1. c
2. c
3. b
4. d
5. a
6. b
7. d
8. a
9. b
10. c
11. c
12. d

True/False

1. F
2. T
3. F
4. T
5. T
6. F
7. F
8. T
9. T
10. F

Fill-In

1. nymphomania
2. domination and submission
3. dominatrix
4. fetishism
5. zoophilia
6. frotteurism
7. voyeurism
8. exhibitionism
9. pedophilia
10. masturbatory asphyxia

Short Answer

1. Pages 387–390
2. Pages 400–402
3. Pages 409–410
4. Pages 415–417

OBSERVATIONS AND REFLECTIONS

OBSERVATION

Does It Happen in My Community?

This activity gives you a chance to find out about paraphilic sexual behavior in the area where you live. Contact your police department and ask to talk to the person in charge of sexually-related crimes.

Ask them about which of the behaviors discussed in the chapter have been reported to authorities within the last year.

Have any reports led to arrests?

Have they seen an increase in any type of sex-related crime?

When people are arrested as exhibitionists or voyeurists, are they usually handled by court action leading to jail or by psychological counseling or both?

What is the attitude of the person you talked to toward people who have paraphilias?

OBSERVATION

The Media and Atypical Sexual Behavior

How are atypical or paraphilic behaviors treated by the media? When they do appear on television, it is usually on crime shows. If you have seen any shows dealing with behaviors discussed in this chapter, answer these questions.

What atypical behavior was shown?

What role did it have in the plot of the program?

What was the attitude that was portrayed about this behavior?

How did you feel about the way it was handled?

A common theme in movies has been cross-dressing. Watch one of the movies that explores this issue such as "Some Like It Hot," "Tootsie," "Torch Song Trilogy," or "Crying Game," and answer these questions.

What are the motives for the cross-dressing?

What role did it have in the plot of the program?

What was the attitude that was portrayed about this behavior?

How did you feel about the way it was handled?

REFLECTION

Sexual Attitudes and Legal Sanctions

This activity gives you the opportunity to examine your feelings and attitudes toward the many sexual activities discussed in this chapter.

Another aspect to look at is the legal sanctions that you feel should occur as a result of each of these activities.

Check the column that best matches the way you feel about each behavior.

Use this key to help you mark the chart:

Attitudes:

A. normal and acceptable
B. acceptable
C. abnormal
D. major psychological disturbance

Legal Sanctions:

A. repeal all laws regulating this activity
B. decriminalize, require treatment
C. misdemeanor, short-term sentence
D. felony, long-term sentence
E. mandatory counseling

	ATTITUDES				LEGAL SANCTIONS				
Sexual Activity	**A**	**B**	**C**	**D**	**A**	**B**	**C**	**D**	**E**
domination and submission									
bondage and discipline									
humiliation									
babyism									
kennelism									
fetishism									
transvestism									
zoophilia									
voyeurism									
exhibitionism									
telephone scatalogia									
frotteurism									
necrophilia									
pedophilia									
sexual sadism and sexual masochism									
sexual addiction									

REFLECTION

People in the News

In the previous exercise you examined your general attitudes toward various sexual behaviors. In this exercise, think about people in the media who have reportedly done some of the activities that can be described as paraphilias. What is your view of them? What is the general view of the public? Who does this person appeal to? You might not be familiar with all the names. Do the ones you know, and you might want to ask other classmates and friends about the others.

Person	Sexual Connection	Your View	Public View	Audience
Madonna				
Woody Alan				
RuPaul				
Richard Gere				
Boy George				
PeeWee Herman				
Michael Jackson				
Van Morrison				
Jerry Lee Lewis				

Can you think of others to add to your list?

When these behaviors (paraphilias) are personalized to someone you have heard of, does it change your views in any way?

After doing this and the previous exercise, how do you feel about where to draw the line between a behavior being an atypical behavior and a paraphilia?

GENDER AND SEXUAL IDENTITY QUESTIONS

- Sometimes I wonder if I am normal because . . . .

- I find the idea of participating in exhibitionist behavior . . . .

- I find the idea of participating in voyeuristic behavior . . . .

- When I think about myself cross-dressing I think . . . .

- I find the idea of participating in domination or submission activities . . . .

- I have encountered a ____ and it made me feel . . . .
  (paraphiliac such as exhibitionist, obscene phone caller)

- I have engaged in sexual practices that may be physically harmful to myself or others when . . . .

- I have engaged in sexual practices that may be psychologically harmful to myself or others when . . . .

- I have/have not gotten into therapy about this because . . . .

I'd been smoking pot regularly since 14 and drinking since about 16. After my fling with the older woman, I began to use more heavily and experimented with hallucinogens and amphetamines. It was just a general trend to try new things that I wasn't supposed to. I was a risk taker. Peer pressure to use drugs and achieve sexual experiences were closely related. I later moved to Berkeley to attend school, but the only education I got was through drugs and sex. —27-year-old Caucasian male

I am no stranger to sexual paraphilias but upon seeing a man's erect penis pointed in my face while I was busily searching for a library book deeply upset me. The exhibitionist chose a most public forum—the local library which was literally attached to the police department. Upon seeing him and observing children studying merely one aisle away, I scrambled to the front desk and asked that the police be called. Hearing my request, the man chose to remain in place and was quickly apprehended. The element of surprise caught me off guard, but the element of guilt appeared to motivate him to choose and remain in a place where his violation could be recognized and punished. I still wonder, sometimes, why this incident upset me so. —44-year-old female Caucasion

CHAPTER 12
CONTRACEPTION AND BIRTH CONTROL

CHAPTER OUTLINE

LEARNING OBJECTIVES

At the conclusion of Chapter 12, students should be able to:

1. Explain the psychology of contraceptive risk taking and discuss the issues involved in choosing a reliable method.
2. List and describe hormonal methods of contraception (including oral contraceptives, implants, and injections) and their effectiveness, advantages, and possible problems.
3. List and describe barrier methods of contraception (including condoms, diaphragms, cervical caps, sponges, and female condoms) and their effectiveness, advantages and possible problems.
4. Describe spermicides (including contraceptive foam, film, creams, and jellies) and their effectiveness, advantages, and possible problems.
5. Describe the IUD (intrauterine device) and its effectiveness, advantages, and possible problems.
6. List and describe fertility awareness methods (including calendar, BBT, mucous method, sympto-thermal) and their effectiveness, advantages, and possible problems.
7. List and describe sterilization methods and their effectiveness, advantages and possible problems.
8. Discuss postcoital birth control methods (including morning-after pill, menstrual extraction, and RU-486) and their effectiveness, advantages, and possible problems.
9. Discuss the future of birth control research, including obstacles and developing technologies.
10. Discuss abortion, including methods, prevalence, characteristics of women having abortions and their reasons, and men and abortion; and delineate the arguments in the abortion debate.

PRACTICE TEST QUESTIONS

Multiple Choice

1. Which is true about the use of birth control?
   a. Most couples use birth control the first time they have intercourse.
   b. Twice as many married women as compared to single women use birth control.
   c. As men and women age they are less likely to use birth control.
   d. The most consistent users of contraception are men and women who explicitly communicate about the subject.

2. Over one year, a couple having unprotected intercourse has what chance of becoming pregnant?
   a. 90%
   b. 70%
   c. 50%
   d. 30%

3. Which of the following is NOT considered a hormonal method of birth control?
   a. the pill
   b. sterilization
   c. Norplant
   d. Depo-Provera or DMPA

4. Which is the most common form of contraception among married couples in the United States?
   a. the pill
   b. the diaphragm
   c. sterilization
   d. the IUD

5. The contraceptive sponge:
   a. blocks the opening of the cervix and releases a spermicide
   b. blocks the opening of the fallopian tubes and releases a spermicide
   c. can be taken out one hour after intercourse
   d. has a lower failure rate among women who have given birth

6. A relatively new spermicidal preparation that is sold as a small translucent tissue is:
   a. contraceptive foam
   b. contraceptive film
   c. RU-486
   d. Depo-Provera or DMPA

7. Birth control methods that also provide some protection against some STDs and infections include all of the following EXCEPT:
   a. condom
   b. sponge
   c. birth control pill
   d. spermicidal foam

8. Which is NOT a common side effect when a women starts taking birth control pills?
   a. breast tenderness
   b. nausea or vomiting
   c. weight gain or loss
   d. smaller breast size

9. The most serious risk to women taking the pill is:
   a. osteoporosis
   b. circulatory disease
   c. ovarian cancer
   d. endometrial cancer
10. The health risks of taking the birth control pill are increased if the woman:
   a. is overweight
   b. smokes
   c. has low blood pressure
   d. has heavy periods
11. The contraceptive implant approved for use in 1990 is called:
   a. RU-486
   b. Depo-Provera
   c. Norplant
   d. nonoxynol-9
12. Which is NOT part of the fertility awareness methods?
   a. calendar (rhythm) method
   b. culpotomy method
   c. basal body temperature method
   d. mucous (Billings) method
13. The most common form of sterilization for women in this country is:
   a. tubal ligation
   b. culpotomy
   c. culdoscopy
   d. hysterectomy
14. According to a report by the American Psychological Association reviewing studies on abortion:
   a. most women felt the most distress after an abortion
   b. a significant number of women reported adverse psychological effects
   c. women felt the most distress preceding an abortion
   d. there has been a significant number of suicides reported after abortions
15. According to the authors' writings on religion and abortion:
   a. the Old Testament clearly states abortion is wrong
   b. the New Testament clearly states abortion is wrong
   c. Moses and Jesus of Nazareth both stated abortion is wrong
   d. the only scriptural basis for or against abortion is inferred or based on interpretation

Fill-Ins

1. ____________________ ____________________ is any means of preventing a birth from taking place, while ____________________ is the prevention of conception altogether.

2. The term used to describe refraining from sexual intercourse is ________________, but it does not mean people can't have other sexual activity that provides sexual satisfaction.

3. The contraceptive implant used to prevent pregnancy for 5 years is commonly known by it trade name of ______________________.

4. Barrier methods of birth control include the ____________________, ____________________, ____________________ ____________________, ____________________, and ____________________ ____________________.

5. A ____________________ is a rubber cup with a flexible rim that is placed inside the vagina blocking the cervix, while a ____________________ ____________________ is a small rubber barrier device that fits snugly over the cervix and is held in place by suction.

6. The most common ingredient used in spermicide sold in the United States is ____________________.

7. The surgical method of abortion that is performed under local anesthesia in the first trimester and uses dilation followed by suction is called ____________________ ____________________.

8. Another method of abortion used in the first trimester is ____________________ ____________________ ____________________, where the cervix is dilated and the uterine wall is scraped.

9. Second trimester methods of abortion include ____________________ ____________________ ____________________, where the cervix is dilated and the fetus removed by alternating solution and curettage.

10. About one-third of all abortions reported in a year in the United States are called ____________________ ____________________, also known as miscarriages.

Note: Some terms may be used more than once.

abstinence	dilation and evacuation (D&E)
birth control	female condom
cervical cap	nonoxynol-9
condom	Norplant
contraception	sponge
diaphragm	spontaneous abortion
dilation and curettage (D&C)	vacuum aspiration

Matching

1. birth control ______
2. contraception _____
3. Norplant _____
4. Depo-Provera (DMPA) _____
5. nonoxynol-9 _____
6. RU-486 _____
7. menstrual extraction _____
8. spontaneous abortion _____

a. The injectable contraceptive which lasts from 3 to 6 months.

b. The most widely used spermicide in the United States.

c. The prevention of conception altogether.

d. Removal of the endometrial contents by suction through a small tube attached to a vacuum pump.

e. Means of preventing birth from taking place.

f. Contraceptive implant that contains progestin implanted under a woman's skin and lasts for 5 years.

g. Commonly referred to as "miscarriages."

h. A new drug that can terminate early pregnancy and is used in China, France, and other countries but not the United States.

Short Answer

1. According to Kristin Luker's study of contraceptive risk taking, why do people take risks? What are the "cost-benefits" of contraceptive use?

2. What are some ways that men can take contraceptive responsibility?

3. Women are buying between 40% to 90% of the condoms sold. What are the four key points concerning women and condom use?

4. What are the factors that influence a woman's decision to have an abortion and what are some possible feelings she may experience concerning the process?

5. Compare and contrast the pro-life and pro-choice arguments.

ANSWERS TO PRACTICE TEST QUESTIONS

Multiple Choice

1. d
2. a
3. b
4. c
5. d
6. b
7. c
8. d
9. b
10. b
11. c
12. b
13. a
14. c
15. d

Fill-In

1. Birth control/contraception
2. abstinence
3. Norplant
4. condom/diaphragm/cervical cap/sponge/female condom
5. diaphragm/cervical cap
6. nonoxynol-9
7. vacuum aspiration
8. dilation and curettage
9. dilation and evacuation
10. spontaneous abortion

Matching

1. e
2. c
3. f
4. a
5. b
6. h
7. d
8. g

Short Answer

1. Page 424
2. Page 427
3. Pages 438–441
4. Pages 464–465
5. Pages 466–468

OBSERVATIONS AND REFLECTIONS

OBSERVATION

What's New in High School?

Try to find a teenager who you can interview to find out if there is a health clinic on the high school campus.

Does it provide birth control counseling?

Does it give out birth control supplies?

If it does, what methods are available?

Is parent permission needed in order to take advantage of services?

Are condoms given out on campus? (Often this is seen as part of "disease prevention" and not birth control.)

Is there a cost to any services or devices?

How does the student feel about the availability of these services and students' utilization of them?

PERSONAL INVOLVEMENT ASSESSMENT

BIRTH CONTROL CONTINUUM

1. Indicate how YOU feel about these birth control methods by placing the number for each method at the appropriate point on the following continuum. Try to enter each one.

1. Abortion
2. Abstinence
3. Condoms
4. Depo-Provera (DMPA)
5. Diaphragm with Cream
6. Foam
7. Female Condom
8. Spermicide with Condom
9. IUD
10. Norplant
11. Nothing
12. Pill
13. Rhythm
14. Sponge
15. Tubal Ligation
16. Vasectomy
17. Withdrawal

Very Unacceptable	**No Feeling**	**Very Acceptable**

|————————————————|————————————————|

2. Using the same list as in number 1, indicate how you feel about others using these methods.

Very Unacceptable	**No Feeling**	**Very Acceptable**

|————————————————|————————————————|

3. Discuss how you feel about using the method you think is most appropriate for yourself. Take into consideration the "hassle factor" of how you feel about touching your body, the cost, safety, and convenience aspects of the method.

OBSERVATION

Abortion: An Issue That Divides

1. Abortion is an issue that people usually feel very strongly about whether they are for it or against it. Take this opportunity to clarify your views. Interview someone who is pro-choice and someone who is anti-abortion (pro-life). Make up a list of questions you will ask each of them including why they hold these views, how they feel about the different legal issues involved, and how they feel about the drug RU-486.

   What is your view before you interview people about this issue?

   What were the main points made by the pro-choice person you interviewed?

   What were the main points made by the anti-abortion person you interviewed?

   Note the language they use when talking about these issues. Listen for words like: pro-abortion, pro-choice, abortion-rights, pro-life, right-to-life, anti-choice, anti-abortion, no-choice. How does this vocabulary affect people's perception of the issue?

   Did hearing the views of each side change your views?

2. Because of all the controversy and recent attacks on the places and the people that do abortions, there are many communities where it is difficult or impossible to find a place to have one done. Call family planning clinics in your area to see of there is access to these types of services. Tell them why you are calling, as many times people who oppose these services call and they might think that is why you are calling!

   Are services available?

   Do they have to deal with any disturbances because of opposition to the services?

REFLECTION

Your Reproductive Life Plan

Birth control must fit into your reproductive life plan. Ask yourself these question to help you work out your personal reproductive life plan:

Would I like to have children one day? (If you answer no, would you describe that as being "childless" or "childfree"?)

Would I like to be married one day?

Would I like to wait until I'm married to start having sexual intercourse?

At what point during or after my education would I like to be married?

How old would I like to be when I have my first child?

How many children would I like to have?

How sad would I be if I were not able to have any children?

How concerned would I be if I were to become pregnant before I were married?

If I were to become pregnant before I wanted to become pregnant, would I consider an abortion?

Would I like to work when my children are toddlers? When my children are in their childhood years? When my children are no longer in the home?

Of all the things I could do in my life, probably the most important for me to accomplish is this:

Children would affect this goal in the following ways:

What would it mean to me if my marriage were to end in divorce?

How does my life plan fit in with my ethical or religious beliefs?

REFLECTION

Taking Sexual Risks

1. After reading the discussion on Kristen Luker's study on risk taking, do you think this applies to you?

   Do you take sexual risks? What kind?

   Do you take risks in other areas of your life? For example, if you were late to an appointment but needed to get gas, would you go on and hope there was enough gas, waiting until on the way home to stop at the gas station?

   Do the two (risk taking in general and risk taking during sex) overlap?

2. After doing the self-assessments in the textbook and study guide about feelings and attitudes toward birth control, what you have learned about what factors are important to you. Knowing your attitudes toward birth control and your attitude toward risk taking, do you think you are likely to "take chances"?

GENDER AND SEXUAL IDENTITY QUESTIONS

After reading the textbook, you have gained some understanding of how attitudes, feelings, and beliefs about birth control and risk taking are affected. If you have been sexually active yourself, answer all these questions that apply to you.

- The first time I had sex I did/didn't use birth control because . . . .

- Looking back I think it was because . . . .

- I usually talk to someone about birth control before/after we have intercourse.

- The reason I do it then is because . . . .

- Talking about birth control with a partner makes me feel . . . .

- My feelings when I went to get birth control from the doctor/clinic were . . . .

- When I bought birth control supplies I felt . . . .

- I (or my partner) have been faced with the decision of abortion, and that was . . . .

- When someone close to me had to deal with abortion . . . .

- My feelings about abortion now are . . . .

I didn't know much about abortion, but I knew that it was a way out and I was going to try anything. I ended up going to my best friend's house to look through her yellow pages in order to find cheap clinics. By doing this, I ended up in one of the worst abortion clinics you could imagine. I remember that there was only one nurse who was also the receptionist and about two doctors at the most. As I lay on the examination table, I remember seeing ants crawling around the place, and it looked like a meat market. As I walked into the actual abortion room, I could see something that held the aborted babies. All I can say at this point of my life is that I am glad to be alive. —22-year-old African-American female

We began to have sex but tried not to have intercourse. We made promises to each other that one person would always keep an article of clothing on to act as a barrier in case our passion got out of control. Well, needless to say, that plan never worked very well. To this day I ask myself why we did not get some type of birth control, especially when we realized our relationship was going to last for a while. It does not take much to figure out the answer to that question. I felt guilty about being in a sexual relationship, and actively pursuing birth control would have meant I knew what I was doing and was choosing to go against what I had been taught was wrong. —33-year-old female Caucasian recalling her first sexual experience with her high school boyfriend. She later became pregnant.

CHAPTER 13
CONCEPTION, PREGNANCY, AND CHILDBIRTH

CHAPTER OUTLINE

Children by Choice
- Child-Free Marriage
- Deferred Parenthood

Fertilization and Fetal Development
- The Fertilization Process
- Development of the Conceptus

Being Pregnant
- Pregnancy Tests
- The Pregnant Woman and Her Partner
- Sexuality During Pregnancy
- Complications of Pregnancy and Dangers of the Fetus
- Diagnosing Abnormalities of the Fetus
- Pregnancy Loss

Infertility
- Female Infertility
- Male Infertility
- Emotional Responses to Infertility
- Infertility Treatment
- Surrogate Motherhood
- *Perspective 1: The Ethics of Reproductive Technology*

Giving Birth
- Labor and Delivery
- Choices in Childbirth
- *Perspective 2: Making a Birth Plan*
- *Perspective 3: The Medicalization of Childbirth*
- The Question of Circumcision
- Breast-feeding
- *Perspective 4: Practical Hints on Breast-feeding*

Becoming a Parent
- The Postpartum Period
- Parental Roles and Stress

LEARNING OBJECTIVES

At the conclusion of Chapter 13, students should be able to:

1. Discuss the motivations for childfree marriage and deferred parenthood.
2. Describe the fertilization process and development of the conceptus.
3. Discuss the pregnant woman's relationship to her partner and sexuality during pregnancy.
4. List and describe the possible complications of pregnancy, including teratogens, diseases, conditions, low birth weight, and fetal diagnosis.
5. Discuss pregnancy loss, including spontaneous abortion, infant mortality rates, and coping with loss.
6. List the principal causes of male and female infertility, and discuss emotional responses to infertility, treatments, surrogate motherhood, and ethical issues.
7. Describe the stages of labor and delivery.
8. Discuss childbirth choices, including hospital births, C-sections, prepared childbirth, birthing rooms and centers, home births, and circumcision.
9. Discuss breast-feeding, including the physiology, benefits, and issues involved in choosing to breast-feed.
10. Discuss becoming a parent, including the postpartum period, parental roles, gay/lesbian parenting, and coping with stress.

PRACTICE TEST QUESTIONS

Multiple Choice

1. The current use of the term "childfree" to replace the term "childless" reflects:
   a. that couples who don't have children today are viewed as lacking fulfillment
   b. the shift of values in our culture that sees not having children as a choice with positive advantages
   c. that women who choose to be childfree are usually poorly educated
   d. none of the above

2 Studies of childfree marriages indicate:
   a. a higher degree of marital adjustment or satisfaction than is found among couples with children
   b. a lower degree of marital adjustment or satisfaction than is found among couples with children
   c. divorce is more probable in childfree marriages
   d. both a and c

3. Since the 1960s:
   a. the age at marriage has steadily increased
   b. more women are waiting till their thirties to begin parenthood
   c. effective birth control has been a factor in delaying parenthood
   d. all of the above

4. If intercourse occurs, fertilization can take place:
   a. no more than 72 hours prior to or 24 hours after ovulation
   b. only within 24 hours before or after ovulation
   c. only within 12 hours before or after ovulation
   d. only within 24 hours after ovulation

5. Pregnancy tests detect the presence of what hormone secreted by the implanted blastocyst?
   a. estrogen
   b. testosterone
   c. HCG (human chorionic gonadotropin)
   d. amnion

6. The trimester of pregnancy where the expectant mother is most likely to experience nausea, fatigue, and swelling of the breasts is usually the:
   a. first trimester
   b. second trimester
   c. third trimester
   d. second trimester if she is having a boy

7. Concerning sexual activity and pregnancy:
   a. most doctors advise no sexual activity for women after the third month of pregnancy
   b. orgasms are considered harmful to most pregnant women after the fifth month of pregnancy
   c. unless a woman has a medical problem, sexual activity should present no problems during pregnancy
   d. most couples have no desire for sexual activity during pregnancy

8. At the present time, most experts counsel pregnant women to:
   a. drink no more than one beer or one glass of wine per day
   b. drink beer, wine, or other alcohol only after the fourth month, since vital organs are already formed
   c. abstain entirely from alcohol because there is no safe dosage known at this time
   d. drink whatever they normally do but stay away from cocaine

9. Cigarette smoking in pregnant women:
   a. has not been shown to affect babies if their mothers smoke less than a pack a day
   b. produces babies who are lighter at birth than babies born to nonsmokers
   c. has been implicated in sudden infant death syndrome, respiratory disorders in children, and various adverse pregnancy outcomes
   d. both b and c

10. To detect toxemia, it is most important that pregnant women:
    a. get their blood pressure checked regularly
    b. get heir iron level checked regularly
    c. have ultrasounds done regularly
    d. have the size of the fetus checked regularly

11. Which test can first reveal whether the fetus has Down syndrome?
    a. amniocentesis
    b. chorionic villus sampling (CVS)
    c. alpha-feto protein (AFP) screening
    d. Apgar score

12. The U.S. infant mortality rate:
    a. is the lowest in the world
    b. ranks 24th among developing nations
    c. often results from poverty
    d. both b and c

13. Concerning infertility:
    a. the overall fertility rate for American women is declining
    b. the greatest increase in infertility is found in couples between the ages 20–24
    c. women's fertility doesn't naturally begin to decline until they reach their forties
    d. all the above are true

14. The longest stage of labor is:
    a. the first stage
    b. the second stage
    c. the third stage
    d. none, they are all equal in time

15. All of the following are true about the postpartum period after the birth of a child EXCEPT:
    a. all women say this is one of the happiest times of their lives
    b. it may create considerable stress
    c. fathers are also affected and feel stress
    d. biological, psychological, and social factors can all affect the postpartum period

Fill-In

1. Instead of the term "childless marriage," which viewed not having children as lacking something essential for personal fulfillment, the term ______________________ marriage is being used more, which reflects a shift of values in our culture that stresses that not having children can be liberating.

2. Substances that cause defects in developing embryos or fetuses are known as ______________________.

3. In an ______________________ pregnancy, the fertilized egg can implant itself in the fallopian tube.

4. The fertility treatment where sperm and oocyte are combined in a laboratory dish and later the pre-embryo is implanted is called ______________________ ______________________ ______________________.

5. The fertility treatment where sperm and eggs are collected and deposited together in the fallopian tube is known as ____________ ____________ ____________.

6. The fertility treatment where semen is deposited by syringe near the opening of the cervix is known as ____________ ____________.

7. The test where fluid from the uterus is tested for birth defects is called ____________.

8. The process of one woman having a baby for another woman is known as ____________ ____________.

9. During labor, the thinning of the cervix is known as ____________.

10. During labor, the widening of the opening of the cervix is known as ____________.

amniocentesis	effacement
artificial insemination	gamete intrafallopian transfer
childfree	in vitro fertilization
dilation	surrogate motherhood
ectopic	teratogens

Matching 1

____ 1. blastocyst — a. The term for the conceptus for the first 8 weeks.

____ 2. embryo — b. The name given a zygote after 4 or 5 days, containing about 100 cells.

____ 3. fetus — c. The term for the human ofspring or conceptus after the eighth week.

____ 4. umbilical cord — d. The organ formed in early pregnancy through which the fetus receives oxygen and nutrients and gets rid of waste.

____ 5. lanugo — e. The fine, downy hair that covers the fetus.

____ 6. chorion — f. The embryo's outermost membrane.

____ 7. placenta — g. The structure that attaches the mother's bloodstream to the fetus.

Matching 2

____ 1. ultrasound — a. Procedure, either through the abdomen or cervix involving removal of tiny pieces of membrane that encase the embryo to test for chromosomal abnormalities.

____ 2. sonogram — b. Procedure where amniotic fluid is withdrawn from the uterus through the abdominal wall of the mother and is tested for chromosomal abnormalities.

____ 3. amniocenteses — c. Uses high-frequency sound waves to create a picture of the fetus in the uterus.

____ 4. chorionic villus sampling (CVS)

____ 5. alpha-feto protein (AFP) screening

d. Test performed on the mother's blood to reveal abnormalities of the fetus's spine, spinal cord, skill, and brain.

e. The picture made by ultrasound of the fetus in the uterus.

Matching 3

____ 1. artificial insemination (AI)

____ 2. therapeutic donor insemination (TDI)

____ 3. in vitro fertilization (IVF)

____ 4. gamete intrafallopian transfer (GIFT)

____ 5. zygote intrafallopian transfer (ZIFT)

a. Egg and sperm are united in a petri dish and then transferred immediately to the fallopian tubes.

b. Sperm and eggs are collected from parents and deposited together in the fallopian tubes.

c. Partner's semen is deposited by syringe near the cervical opening.

d. Sperm from a donor is deposited by syringe near the cervical opening.

e. Combining sperm and oocyte in laboratory dish and then implanting the blastocyst into the uterus.

Short Answer

1. List the variety of feelings that women and their partners may experience during pregnancy. What types of changes can occur in their relationship as a result of the pregnancy?

   Woman:

   Partner:

   Relationship changes:

2. What recommendation and suggestions do doctors usually make concerning sexual behavior during pregnancy?

3. What feelings can pregnant women experience as the result of a loss of pregnancy and/or child before or during birth? What steps can help in the healing process?

4. Describe the emotional responses couples can have to infertility and what treatment options are available.

ANSWERS TO PRACTICE TEST QUESTIONS

Multiple Choice

1. b
2. d
3. d
4. a
5. c
6. a
7. c
8. c
9. d
10. a
11. b
12. d
13. b
14. a
15. a

Fill-Ins

1. childfree
2. teratogens
3. ectopic
4. in vitro fertilization
5. gamete intrafallopian transfer
6. artificial insemination
7. amniocentesis
8. surrogate motherhood
9. effacement
10. dilation

Matching 1

1. b
2. a
3. c
4. g
5. e
6. f
7. d

Matching 2

1. c
2. e
3. b
4. a
5. d

Matching 3

1. c
2. d
3. e
4. b
5. a

Short Answer

1. Pages 489–490
2. Pages 491–492
3. Pages 492–494
4. Pages 515–521

OBSERVATIONS AND REFLECTIONS

OBSERVATION

The Childbirth Experience

Look in the yellow pages of your local telephone book to find childbirth centers available to women. You can look under Childbirth, Hospitals, or Pregnancy to see if you can find any information about what is available in your area. How else might you find assistance in finding a place to have the type of childbirth experience you would like? If you are considering parenthood, call to interview someone at the facilities concerning their approach, philosophy, and medical care of the mother and child.

Facility interviewed:

Philosophy on childbirth:

Philosophy on prenatal care:

Costs involved:

Medical provider:

Would you feel comfortable using this facility? Why or why not?

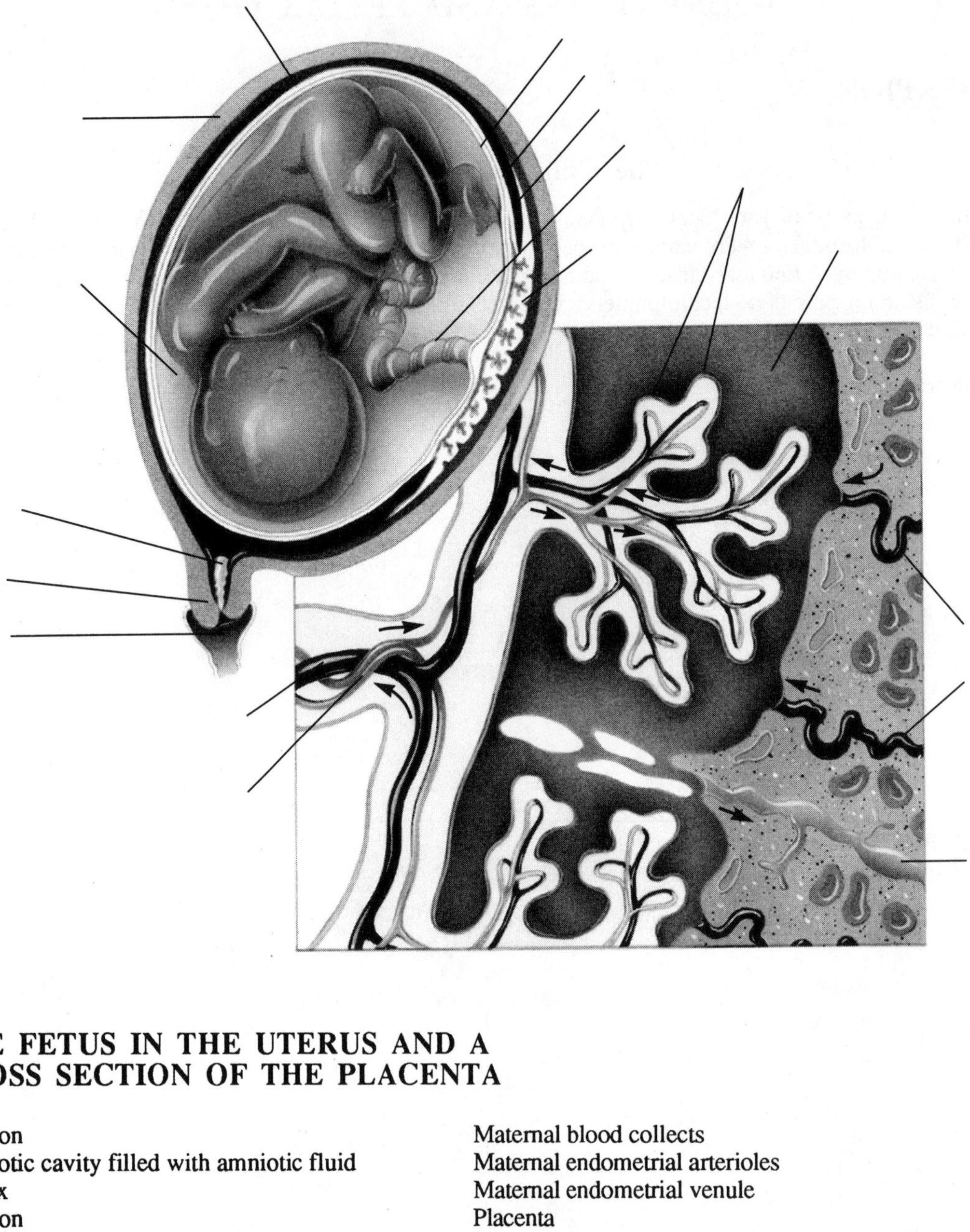

THE FETUS IN THE UTERUS AND A CROSS SECTION OF THE PLACENTA

Amnion
Amniotic cavity filled with amniotic fluid
Cervix
Chorion
Chorionic villi
Lining of uterus (endometrium)
Mucous plug
Muscle layer of uterine wall
Maternal blood collects
Maternal endometrial arterioles
Maternal endometrial venule
Placenta
Umbilical arteries
Umbilical cord
Umbilical vein
Uterine cavity
Vagina (birth canal)

Source: Insel/Roth, 1988. *Core Concepts in Health,* Fifth Edition. Mayfield Publishing Company.

OBSERVATION

The Childbirth Experience

Interview two or three friends who have experienced childbirth and discuss with them their experiences, perceptions, and feelings about the approach they chose.

What aspects of their childbirth experience were similar?

What aspects of their childbirth experience were different?

What suggestions could they give you to prepare for the birth of a baby?

REFLECTION

Thinking About a Childbirth Plan

This chapter discusses the various childbirth options perspective parents have today. The more awareness they have about the options available and the more they reflect upon what is important to them, the more likely that it will be a positive and memorable experience. Even though having a baby may be years away, answering these questions will give you a chance to clarify what is important to you. It is important for couples to think about these issues together, and it helps to make childbirth a more intimate and shared experience. When you come to that point in your life, this can also be a useful list to help you chose medical personnel who share your views and concerns.

Selecting a physician to help you manage and oversee your pregnancy and delivery is a very important process for most women. With men becoming more involved in the birth process, it is also important for their views to be considered. What qualities and background would you look for and desire in a doctor or midwife?

Qualities:

Background: (Should the doctor be an obstetrician/gynecologist? Would you want a midwife?)

On the next page is a checklist to help you consider what you would like for your birth plan. Keep this list so that when you are looking for a health-care provider you can discuss your birth plan and find out if they have similar views. You also need to be sure that the setting you choose—traditional labor and delivery rooms, alternate birth centers within hospitals, or birth centers—will offer the services and facilities that are important to you.

REFLECTION

Birth Plan Options

Check the following questions/issues that are important to you so that when you meet with the doctor, you may address them.

Admission

___ What type of childbirth training do you encourage patients to take?

___ I would like my coach to remain with me throughout the labor and delivery.

___ I desire more than one person present during the delivery.

___ I desire the option (if health permits) to walk during labor.

Labor

___ Do you recommend intravenous fluids be started? When?

___ What pain medications do you commonly use?

___ At what point during the delivery do you use pain medications?

___ If I desire more or less pain medication during my delivery, what might you say?

___ What types of monitoring (internal or external) do you recommend?

Delivery

___ I would like my delivery to take place at ________________ (hospital, alternate birth center in hospital, birthing center, home)

___ If you are not available, who will deliver the baby? (If this occurs, will my birth plan be honored?)

___ What percent of your deliveries are done by C-section?

___ What are your feelings on doing an episiotomy?

___ I would like my partner to stay with me throughout the birthing process.

___ Can we use a camera or videotape during labor and delivery?

The Baby

___ I want/don't want my baby boy circumcised. Is anesthesia used for this procedure?

___ I desire immediate bonding with my baby, no matter what type of delivery occurs.

___ I desire to nurse my baby immediately.

Recovery

___ I desire my baby to room in with me.

___ I do/do not want supplemental feedings for my child.

___ What are the hospital's/center's procedures for visitation?

REFLECTION

Dealing with Infertility

1. After reading over the tests available to detect birth defects, what if any tests would you be most comfortable with?

   What would you do if a test revealed an abnormality?

2. If you and your partner were unable to achieve a pregnancy after one year of unprotected intercourse, which of the techniques discussed in the book would you be willing to try?

   Would you consider surrogate motherhood as an option?

   Would you consider the use of donor sperm?

   Share your thoughts with a friend to elicit his or her reaction.

3. The question of who should pay for fertility treatments is one faced by couples and insurance companies today. Knowing the success rates mentioned in the book, do you think these treatments should be covered by insurance?

   How much money would you be willing to spend in order to achieve a pregnancy?

REFLECTION

Life Without Children?

A recent article stated that less than 6% of women in their childbearing years who were able to have children did not intend to. Our book suggests that marriage without children can be called "childfree" and not "childless." These questions will give you a chance to reflect on your ideas about how you feel about having children.

It has been suggested that we live in a "pronatal" society where attitudes and policies encourage parenthood for everyone. What are some of the messages you have gotten from society about having children?

For a week, take note if radio and television commercials or print advertisements give a pronatal message. Also this week when you watch television, notice if you are aware of any pronatalism in the shows.

Listen to conversations around you. Do you hear any pronatal messages when people talk? (For example, "It's so exciting, she's pregnant" or "I can't wait till you have children.")

What is your attitude toward couples that don't have children?

How would you feel about having a marriage without children?

GENDER AND SEXUAL IDENTITY QUESTIONS

These questions are for those of you who have experienced childbirth or infertility. Answer the questions that are relevant to you.

Females:

- I have had to deal with infertility and that has made me feel . . . .
- During my pregnancy I felt . . . .
- My feelings about my body during pregnancy were . . . .
- The childbirth experience has affected me by . . . .
- During my pregnancy and childbirth my relationship with the baby's father . . . .
- After my pregnancy, my sexuality was affected by . . . .
- Our relationship has been affected by the birth of the baby by . . . .

Males:

- I have had to deal with infertility and that has made me feel . . . .
- During the pregnancy I felt . . . .

- My feelings about my partner's body during pregnancy were . . . .

- The childbirth experience has affected me by . . . .

- During the pregnancy and childbirth my relationship with the baby's mother . . . .

- After the pregnancy, our sexuality was affected by . . . .

- Our relationship has been affected by the birth of the baby by . . . .

During my second semester of college, I realized I was pregnant. The father of the baby was my boyfriend and now my husband. When I found out I was pregnant, my whole world fell apart. My dreams of finishing college and the possibility of getting a volleyball scholarship were crushed. It was definitely the most important and serious event in my whole life. It was hard for me to accept how much my life was going to change. Abortion was not an option for me; I never even considered it although my husband (boyfriend at the time) would have liked me to. I felt very much at peace the moment I realized I really had no other choice but to keep my baby and take care of him. I lived through a lot of embarrassment, I lost some friends, I lost (my boyfriend) for a while, but I was happy with my decision. —33-year-old female Caucasian

My pregnancy was a amazing experience. Watching my body change and feeling this life moving and kicking inside of me was incredible. My husband and I took a Lamaze class, and it really helped prepare us for what was ahead. While it was still a painful experience, having my husband there and sharing the birth of our son is an experience we will never forget and truly a miracle. —28-year-old African American

CHAPTER 14
THE SEXUAL BODY IN HEALTH AND ILLNESS

CHAPTER OUTLINE

Living in our Bodies: The Quest for Physical Perfection
- Fat and Fat Phobia
- Eating Disorders: Anorexia and Bulimia

Sexuality and Aging
- Women's Issues
- *Perspective 1: Assessing Medical Risks*
- Men's Issues

Sexuality and Disability
- Physical Limitations
- *Perspective 2: The Sexual Rights of People with Disabilities*
- Impairment of Sight and Hearing
- Chronic Illness
- Developmental Disabilities

Sexuality and Cancer
- Cancer and Women
- *Perspective 3: Breast Self-Examination*
- *Perspective 4: Breast Reconstruction*
- Cancer and Men
- *Perspective 5: Testicular Self-Examination*

Other Women's Health Issues
- *Perspective 6: The Unkindest Cut? Female Circumcision*
- *Perspective 7: Gynecological Self-Examination*
- Toxic Shock Syndrome
- Endometriosis
- Lesbian Health Issues

Men's Health: Prostatitis

DES Daughters and Sons

Alcohol, Drugs, and Sexuality
- Disinhibition: The Alcohol-and-Sex Connection
- The Effects of Alcohol on Sexuality
- Gay and Lesbian Issues
- Drug Use and Sexuality

LEARNING OBJECTIVES

At the conclusion of Chapter 14, students should be able to:

1. Define and describe the principal eating disorders and their origin, relationship to sexuality, and prevention and treatment.
2. Discuss issues of sexuality and aging, especially menopause for women and slower sexual responses for men.
3. Discuss issues of sexuality and disability with reference to the special needs of those with physical limitations, chronic illness, and developmental disabilities.
4. Discuss issues of sexuality and cancer for women, including its detection, treatment, and psychological impact.
5. Discuss issues of sexuality and cancer for men, including its detection, treatment, and psychological impact.
6. Discuss women's sexual health issues, including toxic shock syndrome, endometriosis, and lesbian health issues.
7. Discuss the practice of female circumcision, including the process, prevalence, effects, and cultural issues.
8. Discuss prostatitis and its detection, treatment, and psychological impact.
9. Discuss the impact of DES on the daughters and sons of women who took it.
10. Describe the effects of alcohol and drugs on sexuality, including their use as disinhibitors, effects, and relationship to sexual risk taking.

PRACTICE TEST QUESTIONS

Multiple Choice

1. Which of the following is true concerning fat?
   a. Obesity is caused by overeating.
   b. Fat does not necessarily cause disease.
   c. Only fat people have a tendency toward compulsive eating.
   d. Fat people are out of control.

2. People with eating disorders:
   a. often have histories of abuse including incest or other sexual abuse
   b. often have ambivalence toward their body and their sexual nature
   c. are trying to become thin to be more sexually attractive
   d. a and b

3. Effects of menopause often include all of the following EXCEPT:
   a. periods of intense warmth and flushing known as hot flashes
   b. increased vaginal lubrication
   c. loss of bone mass due to lowered estrogen levels
   d. thinning of the vaginal walls

4. Normal sexual changes experienced by men in their forties and fifties usually include all of the following EXCEPT:
   a. achieving erections takes more time
   b. ejaculation takes longer
   c. sexual interest and enjoyment decrease greatly
   d. the amount of ejaculate and the force of ejaculation is less

5. Men with spinal cord damage:
   a. can father children even if they are not able to ejaculate
   b. are never able to have erections
   c. are never able to ejaculate
   d. are not interested in sex

6. Most women with spinal cord injuries:
   a. lose all interest in sex
   b. gradually develop multiple sclerosis
   c. menstruate and can become pregnant
   d. eventually fully recover the ability to have vaginal and clitoral orgasms

7. The effects of diabetes on sexuality:
   a. are more negative for women than for men
   b. dramatically affect fertility for men
   c. often include erectile dysfunction
   d. include loss of desire for sex by most diabetic women

8. The following are guidelines for survivors of heart attacks to follow EXCEPT:
   a. resume sexual activities gradually
   b. do not engage in sexual activity before or after vigorous exercise
   c. avoid sexual activity if it is especially hot or cold
   d. avoid having orgasms with any sexual activity

9. The most prevalent form of cancer in women is:
   a. lung cancer
   b. breast cancer
   c. cervical cancer
   d. uterine cancer

10. All of the following are associated with a higher risk of breast cancer EXCEPT:
    a. family history of cancer
    b. history of breast cancer in a close blood relative (mother, sister, etc.)
    c. having small breasts
    d. late childbearing

11. Most breast lumps:
    a. are cancerous
    b. are not cancerous
    c. are a harmless breast condition
    d. both b and c are correct

12. All of the following are true about prostate cancer EXCEPT:
    a. it is common in men under 40
    b. it is the most common form of cancer among men
    c. it can be checked for by having a physician do a digital/rectal exam
    d. there is a blood test to help in diagnosing it

13. Testicular cancer:
    a. has been decreasing in number
    b. is most common among young white men between 20 and 35
    c. can only be detected by a blood test
    d. has a very low cure rate

14. Which statement about DES is FALSE?
    a. It was used to prevent miscarriages.
    b. Mothers who took DES seem to have an increased incidence in reproductive cancers.
    c. Daughters whose mothers took DES should not take oral contraceptives.
    d. Sons of mothers who took DES have not reported any reproductive problems.

15. Alcohol use can put people at high risk for:
    a. unwanted intercourse
    b. sexual violence
    c. risky sexual behaviors
    d. all of the above

True/False

Mark T or F on the line before the question.

____ 1. Ambivalence towards their body and their sexual nature is often found in people with eating disorders.

____ 2. Most women require special medical treatment during menopause.

____ 3. People with disabilities still have sexual feelings.

____ 4. Women with spinal cord injuries can't get pregnant.

____ 5. After a person has a heart attack, they should not have sexual activity that leads to orgasm.

____ 6. Hormone replacement therapy is recommended for all women who go through menopause.

____ 7. Mammograms are recommended only if a woman has a history of breast cancer in her family.

____ 8. Very few lesbians get breast cancer.

____ 9. A Pap test is used to detect breast cancer.

____ 10. Prostate cancer has a high cure rate.

Fill-In

1. The eating disorder characterized by episodes of binging and purging is known as ____________________, whereas ____________________ ________________________ is the eating disorder characterized by a "relentless pursuit of excessive thinness."

2. The period of time, usually between ages 45 to 55, when a woman's menstrual periods become irregular is known as ________________________.

3. The complete cessation of menstruation is called ________________________.

4. The loss of bone mass caused by lowered estrogen levels is known as ________________________.

5. The administration of estrogen, often combined with progestin to deal with the symptoms of menopause, is known as ________________________ ________________________ therapy.

6. Cancer tumors can be either ________________________, which means they are slow developing and remain localized, or ____________________, which means they invade other tissue and disrupt the normal functioning of vital organs.

7. For early detection of breast cancer, the American Cancer Society recommends that all women over 20 perform ________________________ ________________________ once a month, and by age 50 should have annual ________________________, which are low-dose X-ray screenings.

8. Treatments for breast cancer include the removal of the breast known as ________________________ and removal of just the tumor and lymph nodes, which is known as ________________________.

9. The most reliable means of making an early detection of cervical cancer is the ________________________ ________________________, which is done during a pelvic exam and involves scraping cells from the cervix to examine.

10. The surgical removal of the uterus is known as ________________________, and it often is considered an overdone surgery.

11. An infection that allows staph bacteria to multiply in the vagina and has been attributed to the use of tampons is ________________________ ________________________ ________________________.

12. An inflamed prostate gland is otherwise termed ________________________.

13. The phenomenon of activating normally suppressed behaviors that applies to alcohol and sex is known as

________________________.

anorexia nervosa	malignant
benign	mammogram
breast self-examination	mastectomy
bulimia	menopause
climacteric	osteoporosis
disinhibition	Pap test
hormone replacement therapy (HRT)	prostatitis
hysterectomy	toxic shock syndrome (TSS)
lumpectomy	

Short Answer

1. What type of physical and psychological concerns do women have as they go through menopause? What approaches does the book suggest for treating the physical and psychological symptoms?

2. As we age we are more likely to be affected by the chronic illnesses of diabetes, cardiovascular disease, and arthritis. How can these diseases affect sexuality? What can those affected do to continue the expression of their sexuality?

3. What are some of the concerns regarding people with developmental disabilities and their sexuality?

4. What two things can women do to detect breast and reproductive cancers?

5. What should a woman do if her physician suggests a hysterectomy? What can she expect as the results of this operation?

6. What are two approaches to the treatment of prostate cancer, and how successful are they?

ANSWERS TO PRACTICE TEST QUESTIONS

Multiple Choice

1. b
2. d
3. b
4. c
5. a
6. c
7. c
8. d
9. a
10. c
11. d
12. a
13. b
14. d
15. d

True/False

1. T
2. F
3. T
4. F
5. F
6. F
7. F
8. F
9. F
10. T

Fill-In

1. bulimia/anorexia nervosa
2. menopause
3. climacteric
4. osteoporosis
5. hormone replacement (HRT)
6. benign/malignant
7. breast self-examination/mammograms
8. mastectomy/lumpectomy
9. Pap test
10. hysterectomy
11. toxic shock syndrome
12. prostatitis
13. disinhibition

Short Answer

1. Pages 548–550
2. Pages 555–557
3. Page 557
4. Pages 559–561
5. Pages 556–567
6. Paes 568–569

OBSERVATIONS AND REFLECTIONS

OBSERVATION

The Disabled and Sexuality

The disabled are usually treated in the media as if they are not sexual. However, there are some movies that have explored the subject. Rent and watch the movie "Coming Home" or "Scent of A Woman," and answer these questions.

Was the person with the disability shown having sexual feelings?

How did the person handle their sexual feelings?

How did others react to this person's sexual feelings?

Were there any differences in how they dealt with sexuality compared to someone without a disability?

Did the movie change your view of sexuality and disability? If yes, how was it changed?

OBSERVATION

Mammography

Call your local American Cancer Society and ask them for referrals for places that do mammography. Call one of the places they suggest and ask the following questions.

How much do they charge for a mammogram?

Are the fees usually covered by insurance?

What percent of the mammograms they do are routine screenings suggested for women after age 40?

What percent of the mammograms are done because the woman or her doctor have felt a lump?

If you know a woman over 40 that you would be comfortable discussing this with, ask her these questions.

Have you had a mammogram?

If yes, what was the experience like?

If no, why haven't you had one?

OBSERVATION

Looking for the Perfect Body

The media sends us many messages about standards of beauty. These images can influence how we feel about our own bodies. In different eras or different cultures, the standards of beauty have varied. There have been cultures and times where heavy women were considered the most beautiful. Today the trend is to ultra-thin models. Look through magazines and cut out pictures of both men and women. (You may want to use them to make a collage to share with your class.) Answer these questions about the pictures.

Female pictures:

Does there seem to be an ideal body type that is used the most?

What are the characteristics of that body including:

breast size
type of figure
age
ethnicity
other

Do any models have bodies that suggest anorexia?

Male pictures:

Does there seem to be an ideal body type that is used the most?

What are the characteristics of that body including:

chest size
facial and body hair
type of figure
age
ethnicity
other

Do any of the males have bodies that suggest steroid use?

Do you feel looking at these ads influences how you feel about your body and your sexuality? Remember the effect these images have on us is not always something we are conscious of.

Jane Pratt, the editor of *Sassy,* a magazine for teenage girls, has said that the recent trend to thinner models has led to more girls wanting to diet. Show a teenage girl the pictures you have collected and ask her what she thinks is the ideal body.

REFLECTION

The Unkindest Cut

Our book discusses in Perspective 6 the customs of clitorectomy, female circumcision, and infibulation. Do you think people in our country should actively try to prevent this from going on in other countries or among certain groups in our country?

How would you react if a friend shared with you that this procedure (female circumcision) had been done to her?

How would you react if this friend also told you it was the custom of her country and she felt it should be done to her daughters also?

How would you answer the argument that things we do in our country (breast implants, male circumcision) might be considered mutilating, barbaric, and unnecessary surgeries by people from other cultures?

GENDER AND SEXUAL IDENTITY QUESTIONS

Answer those following questions that are relevant to you.

- Society's emphasis on weight and beauty has affected me by . . . .

- I had an eating disorder when . . . .

- My sexuality is affected by my feeling about my body when . . . .

- When I think about my body aging I feel . . . .

- I have had my health interfere with my sexuality when . . . .

- The effect(s) of drugs and/or alcohol on my sexuality has/have been . . . .

Female question:

I do/do not do breast-self examination because . . . .

Male question:

I do/do not do testicular self-examination because . . . .

Every year I see growth and change in myself. Facing the hurdle of breast cancer was a real test, and I met the challenge. I love the support of my family and friends, but I also enjoy my ability to live happily on my own. —47-year-old female Caucasian

At the age of 36, I was diagnosed with breast cancer and had a breast removed. At that time I was not as concerned with the way that I would look as I was with the chance that I might die from this thing eating me away. My husband has always been there for me through all of the years we have dealt with this, as has my son. I never felt that anyone was repulsed by my changed body, but rather was concerned that I was well and there with them. I never felt that my breast was the only part of me that was important to my husband, nor was it the thing that made me a woman. Our sex life didn't change at all as a result of the loss of the breast, and in comparing the time before I had reconstruction to the time after, I think that there was really no appreciable difference attributable to my having or not having two breasts. There has certainly been no negative change in my attitude. If anything, I may enjoy sex even more knowing how precious each moment of life is. — 45-year-old female Caucasian

There are so many things that have affected my sexual identity—my diabetes, my eating disorder, my negative body image and this underlying pressure of having to be perfect. *It is my own pressure; I can't keep blaming people or things. I have to fix it!* —27-year-old female Caucasian

CHAPTER 16
SEXUALLY TRANSMITTED DISEASES

CHAPTER OUTLINE

X-Rated Diseases: The Psychological Impact of STDs
- Ambivalence About Sexuality
- *Self-Assessment: STD Attitude Scale*
- What's in a Name? VD and STDs

The STD Epidemic
- Social Factors
- Biological Factors
- STD Prevalence
- The Epidemiology of STDs

Principal STDs
- Chlamydia
- Gonorrhea
- Genital Warts
- Genital Herpes
- Syphilis
- *Perspective 1: The Tuskegee Syphilis Study*
- Hepatitis
- Urinary Tract Infections (NGU/NSU)
- Vaginal Infections
- *Perspective 2: Maintaining Vaginal Health*
- Parasites
- Other STDs

STDs and Women
- Biological Sexism
- Pelvic Inflammatory Disease (PID)
- Cystitis
- *Perspective 3: Preventing and Treating Cystitis*

Preventing STDs
- Risk Taking
- Abstinence
- Good Health, Safer Sex
- *Perspective 4: Safer and Unsafe Sexual Practices*
- The Health Belief Model
- STDs and Communication
- *Perspective 5: A Visit to an STD Clinic*

STDs and Public Policy

LEARNING OBJECTIVES

At the conclusion of Chapter 16, students should be able to:

1. Discuss societal ambivalence concerning STDs.
2. List and describe the social and biological factors contributing to the increase in the incidence of STDs.
3. Define risk factor, risk marker, and core group, and give examples of each.
4. List and describe the principal STDs (chlamydia, gonorrhea, genital warts, genital herpes, syphilis, hepatitis, urinary and vaginal infections, and parasitic infestations), including incidence, symptoms, and treatment.
5. Discuss the Tuskegee syphilis study and its impact on contemporary attitudes of African Americans toward public health agencies.
6. Discuss the impact of STDs on women, including "biological sexism," pelvic inflammatory disease (PID), and cystitis.
7. Discuss factors involved in STD prevention, including risk taking, abstinence, and safer sex.
8. Describe the components of the health belief model and give examples of each.
9. Discuss the role of interpersonal communication in preventing STD transmission.
10. Describe public policy measures that could reduce the incidence of STDs.

PRACTICE TEST QUESTIONS

Multiple Choice

1. Which is *not* a social or cultural factor that contributes to the spread of STDs?
   a. education efforts that are hampered by vocal minorities
   b. a health-care system that cannot meet our needs, especially in urban areas
   c. many people still don't use condoms
   d. many STDs don't have symptoms

2. Which of these statements about STDs is FALSE?
   a. Most STDs are preventable.
   b. Almost all STDs are curable.
   c. You can have an STD and have no symptoms.
   d. STDs are always transmitted sexually.

3. Which of the following is a risk factor, and not a risk marker for STDs?
   a. a large number of sex partners
   b. ethnicity
   c. place of residence
   d. socioeconomic status

4. Which of the following statements about chlamydia is TRUE?
   a. It usually starts with a chancre.
   b. Most women show recognizable symptoms to chlamydia.
   c. It is the most common STD in the United States.
   d. It cannot be cured.

5. People who are sexually active with several partners:
   a. should get a screening for STDs if they notice symptoms
   b. should get a screening for STDs if they think their partner has an STD
   c. should get a screening for STDs every 3 to 6 months
   d. should get a screening for STDs every 2 years

6. For most sexually transmitted diseases:
   a. men and women are equally likely to have symptoms
   b. men are more likely than women to have symptoms
   c. women are more likely than men to have symptoms
   d. only men and women over age 20 have symptoms

7. The treatment for gonorrhea is usually:
   a. penicillin
   b. laser therapy
   c. podophyllin
   d. acyclovir

8. Which of the following is caused by exposure to human papilloma virus?
   a. chlamydia
   b. gonorrhea
   c. genital warts
   d. syphilis

9. It is estimated that 1 out of every __________ Americans over age 15 carries the herpes simplex virus.
   a. 7
   b. 70
   c. 700
   d. 7000

10. Which STD can be prevented by a vaccination?
    a. chlamydia
    b. hepatitis B
    c. gonorrhea
    d. syphilis

True/False

Mark T or F on the line by the question.

____ 1. One of the factors that contributes to the high incidence of STDs in the United States is our ambivalence about sexuality.

____ 2. Genital warts are treated with penicillin.

____ 3. Genital herpes is caused by a bacteria.

____ 4. The drug that can help in reducing or suppressing herpes symptoms is acyclovir.

____ 5. Syphilis has almost been eradicated as a disease because of penicillin.

____ 6. Vaginitis always occurs as a result of sexual activity.

____ 7. Barrier methods of birth control, like the sponge or diaphragm, provide more protection against STDs than the birth control pill.

____ 8. Cystitis primarily affects men.

____ 9. The "Tuskegee experiment" is considered a model of how public health research should be done.

____ 10. The health belief model can help us better understand the role of denial in the transmission of STDs.

Fill-In

1. The study of how diseases spread and can be controlled is known as ____________________.

2. The term that implies a *causal* relationship between certain individual characteristics and the likelihood of exposure to disease is ____________________ ____________________ while the term ____________________ ____________________ often includes demographic characteristics as a detail that is not *causally* related.

3. A bladder infection that affects mainly women and is often related to sexual activity is ____________________.

4. The most prevalent STD in the United States and a primary cause of infertility and ectopic pregnancy is ____________________.

5. The STD that is sometimes called "the clap" or "drip" and that may manifest itself by causing painful urination and/or discharge is ____________________.

6. The viral STD that has symptoms which can range from being almost undetectable inside the vagina to miniature cauliflowers on the penis is ____________________ ____________________.

7. Just prior to an outbreak of herpes is a period of a few days when the virus is active and shedding known as the ____________________.

8. The sexually transmitted disease that starts with a chancre is ____________________.

9. The viral disease that affects the liver and can be sexually transmitted is ____________________.

10. An inflammation of the urethra is called ____________________.

chlamydia	prodrome
cystitis	risk factor
epidemiology	risk marker
genital warts	syphilis
gonorrhea	urethritis
hepatitis	

Short Answer

1. What are two social and/or cultural factors that contribute to the spread of STDs?

2. Name and briefly describe two biological factors that contribute to the transmission of STDs.

3. Describe the four stages of syphilis that will occur if it is not treated.

4. Explain what is meant by "biological sexism," and give two reasons why it exists.

5. List three specific health behaviors that help protect us from STDs.

6. List four of the public policy measures that would help to reduce the incidence of STDs.

ANSWERS TO PRACTICE TEST QUESTIONS

Multiple Choice

1. d
2. d
3. a
4. c
5. c
6. b
7. a
8. c
9. a
10. b

True/False

1. T
2. F
3. F
4. T
5. F
6. F
7. T
8. F
9. F
10. T

Fill-In

1. epidemiology
2. risk factor/risk marker
3. cystitis
4. chlamydia
5. gonorrhea
6. genital warts
7. prodrome
8. syphilis
9. hepatitis
10. urethritis

Short Answer

1. Pages 632–633
2. Page 633
3. Pages 643–646
4. Pages 652–653
5. Page 656
6. Pages 661–664

OBSERVATIONS AND REFLECTIONS

OBSERVATION

Where to Go for Help

What types of resources are available in your community for the treatment of STDs? Where could you go, or send a friend who was worried and needed to be treated or get tested? Find out what types of services your college health clinic offers by calling and asking for the range of services and their prices. Also look in the telephone book to see what types of public services are available. Call one or two offices and inquire about the fees, services, and policy regarding anonymity and confidentiality.

After researching the alternatives, where would you go or send your friend?

Why did you choose this facility?

Name of agency: Phone number:

Address:

Services:

Fees:

Comments: (for example, how it felt to call, attitude of people you talked to, etc.)

OBSERVATION

You Spend the Money!

If you could control the budget for your state on spending for STDs, what percentage would you give for each of these programs?

PROGRAM	PERCENTAGE OF YOUR BUDGET
Developing educational programs for schools	_______
Free distribution of condoms	_______
Clinics to treat STDs	_______
Outreach prevention programs to "high-risk groups"	_______
Contact tracing and partner notification programs	_______
Research projects to develop new diagnostic techniques, treatments, vaccines	________
Total	100%

For which program did you allocate the most funding? Why?

For which program did you allocate the least funding? Why?

REFLECTION

What's Your Risk?

There are many factors that influence someone's risk of getting an STD. Some of these are risk factors while others are risk markers. This can give you some idea of what your risk is of getting a sexually transmitted disease. Get out your calculator.

1. Begin with zero.
2. If your age is 11–15, add 5 points.
3. If your age is 16 or over, add 7 points.
4. Add 3 points for each sex partner during the last year.
5. Subtract 1 point for each partner you knew for at least 6 months before having sex.
6. Subtract 1 point for each partner with whom you discussed STDs and risk factors.
7. Subtract:

   3 points if you do or would use a condom with every sexual contact
   2 points if you would use a condom at least half of the time
   1 point if you would only use a condom sometimes
8. Subtract 2 points if you understand STD symptoms and would seek help immediately after identifying one.

Got your score? Here is how it can be evaluated:

Low risk	0–5
Moderate risk	6–10
Serious risk	11+

Answer these questions:

Did the rating this gave you compare with what you would have guessed?

Did you underestimate or overestimate what your risk would be?

Why do you think you did?

If your score is over 5, what could you do to bring it down? How would you feel about doing that?

Adapted from American Social Health Association, 260 Sheridan Ave., Palo Alto, CA 94306.

REFLECTION

Feelings About STDs

As the textbook makes clear, STDs are viewed very differently than are other communicable diseases such as a cold. Complete the following sentences as honestly as you can to clarify your feelings, attitudes, and beliefs about STDs.

1. If I had an STD, I would feel . . . .

2. If I had an STD, I would tell __________ (mother, father, sister/brother, partner, family doctor, doctor at a clinic, doctor at school health service, friends, religious counselor, a counselor, anonymous hot line). Write which ones you would tell in the order you would tell.

3. If my good friend told me he/she had an STD I would feel . . . .

4. My feelings about my friend would/would not change because . . . .

5. If my partner told me he/she had an STD I would feel . . . .

6. My feelings about my partner would/would not change because . . . .

7. If my sister/brother told me they had an STD, I would feel . . . .

8. My feelings about my sister/brother would/would not change because . . . .

9. When I think of people who have STDs I think that they . . . .

Look over this list and see if it gives you more insight into how you view STDs.

GENDER AND SEXUAL IDENTITY QUESTIONS

Having a sexually transmitted disease can definitely affect a person's self-concept and relationships. If this has happened to you or someone you have a sexual relationship with, examining your feelings by answering these questions can help you put it into perspective.

- I found out I had ______________ when . . . .

- I had/had not suspected that I had an STD.

- My first reaction was . . . .

- Later I felt . . . .

- The first person I told was . . . .

- I have not told anyone because . . . .

- My feelings about sex changed/did not change since I found out because . . . .

- I have found that telling people about it . . . .

- My sexual partner told me that he/she had an STD when . . . .

- It was before/after we had sex and so I felt . . . .

- It changed/didn't change our relationship because . . . .

What was I thinking? I had a few boyfriends throughout college, but I did not take my relationships seriously. Towards the end of college I had my last casual sex experience. Sadly I did not think twice about sleeping with those guys until I contracted an STD from the last one. The disease I contracted was genital warts, and it was horrible. The student health center on campus treated the warts with acid and did nothing else. After graduating, I moved and went to a private doctor. The warts were so bad that laser surgery was necessary. Unfortunately, I now have to go to the gynecologist twice a year because I am at a greater risk for cervical cancer because of the warts, number of sex partners, and sex at an early age. —30-year-old female Caucasian

When I was fourteen, my grandfather talked to me about venereal disease. He explained to me about the types of sexually transmitted diseases and that the more sex partners I had the greater the risk of catching an STD. He told me to choose my partners carefully. He also said I should use condoms.

About two weeks later I met a girl. We decided that we wanted to be each other's first sex partner. I took my grandfather's advice and went to a drugstore and bought a box of Trojan condoms. My mom found out that I had sex. She was disappointed but was glad I used protection. —23-year-old male Caucasian

CHAPTER 17
HIV AND AIDS

CHAPTER OUTLINE

Perspective 1: AIDS Myths, AIDS Facts

What Is AIDS?
- Conditions Associated with AIDS
- The Immune System
- The Virus
- AIDS Pathogenesis: How the Disease Progresses

Epidemiology and Transmission of HIV
- Epidemiology of HIV/AIDS
- Myths and Modes of Transmission
- Sexual Transmission
- IV Drug Use
- Mother-to-Child Transmission
- Uncommon Modes of Transmission
- Factors Contributing to Infection

AIDS Demographics
- The Gay Community
- Women and Children
- Teenagers
- Poverty, Ethnicity, and HIV

Education and Prevention
- Protecting Ourselves
- *Self-Assessment: HIV Prevention Attitude Scale*
- *Perspective 2: Learning to Love Latex*
- Getting the Word Out
- HIV Testing

Treatment and Research
- Existing Treatments
- AIDS Research
- Drug Testing

Living with HIV or AIDS
- Discrimination and HIV
- If You Are HIV-Positive
- *Perspective 3: After You've Tested Positive*

LEARNING OBJECTIVES

At the conclusion of Chapter 17, students should be able to:

1. List and describe the conditions and symptoms that may be associated with HIV or AIDS.
2. Describe the principal components and functions of the immune system, the characteristics of the human immuneodeficiency virus, and the process and progress of HIV infection.
3. Explain how HIV can and cannot be transmitted and discuss behaviors that put one at risk.
4. Discuss the effects of the AIDS epidemic on the gay community, including social, political, and psychological factors.
5. Discuss HIV/AIDS issues as they relate to women, children, and adolescents.
6. Discuss the AIDS epidemic in relationship to socioeconomic status and ethnicity.
7. Explain how to protect oneself against HIV infection and describe the principal types of HIV tests.
8. Discuss the issues surrounding HIV/AIDS education and prevention programs.
9. Describe the basic medical treatments for HIV and AIDS and discuss the impact of government policy on AIDS research.
10. Discuss issues surrounding living with AIDS, including discrimination and individual needs.

PRACTICE TEST QUESTIONS

1. The most common opportunistic infection of people with AIDS is:
   a. Kaposi's sarcoma
   b. Pneumocystic carinii pneumonia
   c. tuberculosis
   d. wasting syndrome
2. The white blood cells that play a major role in defending the body against invading organisms and cancerous cells are known as:
   a. reverse transcriptase
   b. lymphocytes
   c. leukocytes
   d. retroviruses
3. An important indicator of how the immune system is functioning is:
   a. the number of helper T cells
   b. the number of killer B cells
   c. the number of macrophages
   d. the number of helper B cells
4. HIV antibodies are usually detectable in the blood how soon after the virus is in the body?
   a. 2–6 hours
   b. 2–6 days
   c. 2–6 months
   d. 2–6 years
5. Physicians and scientists first recognized the new disease that is now known as AIDS in:
   a. 1971
   b. 1977
   c. 1981
   d. 1987
6. Which form of sexual interaction presents the most risk for spreading HIV among men and women?
   a. anal intercourse
   b. vaginal intercourse
   c. oral sex
   d. all the above are equally risky
7. Woman with HIV:
   a. tend to be diagnosed earlier than men with the disease
   b. have had more experimental drugs and medical treatments than men
   c. often have to deal with issues of poverty and racism
   d. are more likely to be lesbian than heterosexual
8. In testing for HIV infection:
   a. the Western blot is given first and the ELISA is used to recheck positives
   b. the ELISA is given first and the Western blot is used to recheck positives
   c. the only test used now is the DNA-HIV
   d. the DNA-HIV is given first and the ELISA is used to recheck positives
9. The direction that AIDS research, treatment, and services takes is most influenced by:
   a. the types of physicians and scientists who go into the field
   b. the amount of money biomedical companies are willing to invest
   c. government policy on these issues
   d. the United Nations policy on these issues

10. The most widely used drug to treat AIDS is:
    a. ddi
    b. ddc
    c. RDI
    d. AZT

11. The three basic types of medical treatments for HIV and AIDS include all of these EXCEPT:
    a. therapies to treat the symptoms and infections
    b. drugs that affect the virus in some way
    c. heat treatments that immobilize the virus
    d. therapies that boost the immune system

12. People with HIV and AIDS have faced discrimination:
    a. in housing
    b. from medical caregivers
    c. from courts and government agencies
    d. all of the above

True/False

Mark T or F on the line before the question.

____ 1. The only difference between someone who is HIV-positive and someone who has AIDS is how long they have had the disease.

____ 2. White fuzzy spots on the tongue are usually the first sign of HIV infection.

____ 3. HIV can live and replicate in water.

____ 4. HIV can be transmitted through oral sex between heterosexuals, gay men, or lesbians.

____ 5. All children born to mothers who are HIV-positive will also be HIV-positive by age 2.

____ 6. If you belong to a demographic group that is at low risk for HIV, you do not have to be concerned about getting infected as long as you avoid anal sex and people in high-risk groups.

____ 7. Because they have strong immune systems, sexually active teenagers are at low risk for contracting HIV.

____ 8. African Americans and Latinos are getting AIDS at a disproportionately higher rate than that of other Americans.

____ 9. The number of helper T cells (called T4 count) in an individual's body is an important indicator of how well the immune system is functioning.

____ 10. Public health officials estimate that by the year 2000, the numbers of women and men who test positive for HIV will be equal.

Fill-In

1. AIDs is an acronym for ____________________ ____________________ ____________________

    ____________________.

2. We call the diseases that take advantage of a weakened immune system ____________________

    ____________________.

3. The type of cancer that causes red or purple blotches to appear under the skin and is more common in gay or bisexual men infected with AIDS is ____________________ ____________________.

4. Large molecules that are capable of stimulating the immune system and then reacting with the antibodies that are released to fight them are called ____________________.

5. Viruses with the ability to reverse the normal genetic writing process are known as ____________________.

6. The process in which a person develops antibodies is called ____________________.

7. Conditions such as drug use, poor nutrition, and smoking that *may* make a person who is HIV-positive more likely to develop AIDS are known as ____________________.

8. Infection of HIV via the bloodstream is called ____________________ ____________________.

9. Infection of HIV from a mother to child in the womb is known as ____________________ ____________________.

10. The most common simple blood test for HIV is called the ____________________ test.

acquired immune deficiency syndrome	opportunistic infections
antigens	parenteral transmission
cofactors	perinatal transmission
ELISA	retroviruses
Kaposi's sarcoma	seroconversion

Short Answer

1. List four myths about ways that AIDS can be transmitted.

2. What are three factors that put women at a higher risk for contracting HIV?

3. Discuss three specific cofactors that may make a person who is HIV-positive more likely to develop AIDS.

4. Describe how the gay community has reacted overall to the AIDS epidemic. Include in your answer a project that has been organized to commemorate those who have died from AIDS.

5. Describe two effective outreach programs that are being tried to reach specific high-risk groups for HIV.

ANSWERS TO PRACTICE TEST QUESTIONS

Multiple Choice

1. b
2. c
3. a
4. c
5. c
6. a
7. c
8. b
9. c
10. d
11. c
12. d

True/False

1. F
2. F
3. F
4. T
5. F
6. F
7. F
8. T
9. T
10. T

Fill-In

1. acquired immune deficiency syndrome
2. opportunistic infections
3. Kaposi's sarcoma
4. antigens
5. retroviruses
6. seroconversion
7. cofactors
8. parenteral transmission
9. perinatal transmission
10. ELISA

Short Answer

1. Pages 680–681
2. Pages 682 and 687
3. Page 687
4. Pages 687–690
5. Pages 698–700

OBSERVATIONS AND REFLECTIONS

OBSERVATION

The School Board Is Called to Order

Imagine that you are a member of the local school board, and the issue has been raised about whether condoms should be distributed in your local high school. Tonight at the meeting they are going to be asking for your view on the subject. Do you feel they should be available and if so, how should they be distributed? Write out what you will state as your position and how you will defend it.

There is also a discussion at the meeting about what age AIDS education should begin and how explicit it should be at each grade level. Parents are raising objectives because they don't want discussions of homosexuality, anal sex, and oral sex included in the schools. Others feel that it is necessary to give proper education on these subjects.

What are you going to state as your general position on these issues?

At what grade level do you think these issues need to be discussed? Make an X in those grades where you think it should be taught. You can mark more than one grade for each subject:

Subject	**Early Elementary (K-3)**	**Late Elementary (4–6)**	**Middle School (7–8)**	**High School (9–12)**
AIDS				
Other STDs				
Homosexuality				
Condoms				
Anal Sex				
Oral Sex				

OBSERVATION

Listening for AIDS Messages

Sensitizing oneself to an issue is a key factor in being able to understand and make decisions about that issue. For one week take note of every message about AIDS you see or hear in advertisements, in news stories, on radio, television, in movies, and in conversation. Record them below:

Did you see or hear very much on the topic?

From what sources did you see or hear the most about AIDS?

If you knew that you were HIV-positive, how might you feel about what you heard or saw?

Do you feel that the media and public are sensitive to this issue?

After listening carefully over the last week, what can you say about your knowledge and feelings about this epidemic? Have they changed?

OBSERVATION

Putting a Face on AIDS

The textbook discusses how outreach programs utilize people with HIV or people with AIDS to speak to groups in order to personalize the HIV epidemic. If you have not heard such a presentation, renting the video "Common Threads—The Story of the Quilt" is a way to share a similar experience. If panels of the quilt come to your area, going to see them will be another way to experience the personal side of this disease. If you are able to do that or have had another personal experience with a person with AIDS or person with HIV, you can write your reaction here.

REFLECTION

What's It Like to Buy Condoms at a Store?

One of the reasons that people don't use condoms is that they are embarrassed to go buy them. Students have written that they drove over 50 miles to go where they wouldn't be recognized to buy condoms. Others have said that the only thing they ever stole in their life was condoms. (In fact, drug stores report that they are a frequently stolen item.) If doing this exercise alone sounds uncomfortable, try to find a classmate or friend to do it with you.

Go to a drugstore and examine the various condoms. As you gather this information, be aware of the feelings you are experiencing. If you are in an area with a condom specialty store like *Condomania,* you could go visit that instead. It's up to you whether or not you want to purchase any. If you do, you can include your reactions to that.

Where in the store are the condoms displayed?

Is it a good location?

Is it a visible location?

Is it too public or too hidden? (Do you think people will easily find the display and then feel comfortable standing there?)

What types are available?

What is the range of prices available?

Were foreign brands like the ones discussed in the textbook displayed?

How did it feel standing in the aisle looking at condoms?

If you bought any condoms, how did that feel?

REFLECTION

Making Choices: Where to Put the Money?

Our book talks about the funding for AIDS compared to that of other diseases such as cancer. If you could allocate money, which of these diseases would you spend the most on?

AIDS

Cancer

Heart Disease

Accident Prevention

Alcoholism

Explain why you made that choice?

Which would you spend the least on?

Why did you make that choice?

REFLECTION

HIV Prevention Attitude Scale

Do the Self-Assessment entitled "HIV Prevention Attitude Scale" located on page 694 in your textbook.

Do you feel it was an accurate measure of how positive your preventative attitudes are? Why?

Looking back over the statements, do you feel reading the chapter had any effect on your attitudes, or were they the same before reading the chapter?

If any attitudes have changed, to what do you attribute the change?

REFLECTION

Testing for HIV?

Our book discusses the feelings that people experience when they decide to get tested for HIV. There are two types of testing: anonymous and confidential. Anonymous testing is when you go to a testing site and do not give your name. You are only identified by a number and when you come back to get your result you again only give your number. In confidential testing you give your name, but there are strict laws that restrict access to others who may try to obtain that information.

After reading this chapter, has it changed your view on whether you need to be tested?

If you decided to be tested would you choose an anonymous or confidential test site? Why?

Look at the exercise entitled "What's Your Risk" in Chapter 16 of this book. Does your decision to be tested or not agree with your rating? (People with moderate or serious risk should consider testing.) If it doesn't, how do you explain your decision?

If you have a friend who has had eight partners over the last two years, including four that were "one-night stands," would you want that friend to be tested?

Do you think you could approach this subject with that friend?

If yes, how would you do it?

If you couldn't approach your friend, explain why.

GENDER AND SEXUAL IDENTITY QUESTIONS

- I remember the first time I heard about AIDS was when I was about __________ years old.

- My first thoughts about it were . . . .

- I thought the chances that anyone I knew would ever be affected were . . . .

- When I heard that Rock Hudson, Magic Johnson, or [another famous person] got AIDS I felt . . . .

- As I got older my views about AIDS changed/did not change so that I now feel . . . .

- I have known/not known anyone with AIDS and this has affected me by . . . .

- AIDS has changed my life by . . . .

- I have/have not been tested for AIDS because . . . .

- To prevent AIDS I . . . .

In the fall of 1985, my father became ill. He was hospitalized frequently, but the doctors did not know what was wrong. My father was a jolly man (he weighed about 268 lbs and stood 5'11"). During his last year, he lost significant amounts of weight. He was changing in front of our eyes not only physically but mentally as well. The disease that was taking over his body was taking over his mind and personality as well. He had become so debilitated that he could attend my high school graduation only for a short time and in a wheel chair. One week later he was taken to Stanford Medical Center where they diagnosed him with AIDS. He died five days later. This was so difficult and still is so difficult to deal with. My mother was astounded. She knew their relationship was not normal but had absolutely no idea he was gay. They had been married for 20 years and without a sexual relationship for 14 years. All that time my mom thought there was something wrong with her. My father led a hidden life. I may not have known his whole person, but the part of the man I knew, I loved. He was a great father. I miss him. I miss him so much!
—23-year-old female Caucasian

I am worried about AIDS because my doctor says that usually condyloma (which was recently diagnosed) is sexually transmitted. The pain I feel inside is overwhelming. The last and fourth time I had sex with him was in December, 1992. I had an AIDS test in February, 1993, and it came out negative. It should have made me feel better; however, it did not. The six-month window period will be over in June; however, I think that I am going to take one in May and in June, just to ease my heart. —21-year-old African-American female

CHAPTER 18
SEXUAL COERCION: HARASSMENT, AGGRESSION, AND ABUSE

CHAPTER OUTLINE

Sexual Harassment
- Flirtation Versus Harassment
- *Perspective 1: The Clarence Thomas / Anita Hill Hearings: Differing White and African American Perspectives*
- Harassment in School and College
- Sexual Harassment in the Workplace

Anti-Gay/Lesbian Harassment, Prejudice, and Discrimination
- Heterosexual Bias
- Anti-Gay Prejudice
- Ending Anti-Gay Prejudice

Sexual Aggression
- Rape
- Forms of Rape
- *Perspective 2: Rape Myths*
- *Perspective 3: Preventing Sexual Assault*
- Motivations for Rape
- The Aftermath of Rape

Child Sexual Abuse
- *Perspective 4: Child Sexual Abuse Myths*
- General Preconditions for Sexual Abuse
- Forms of Intrafamilial Sexual Abuse
- Children at Risk
- Effects of Child Sexual Abuse
- Treatment Programs
- Preventing Sexual Abuse

LEARNING OBJECTIVES

At the conclusion of Chapter 18, students should be able to:

1. Discuss the issues surrounding the definition of sexual harassment, including the difference between flirtation and harassment.
2. Describe the different ways sexual harassment takes place in schools, colleges, and the workplace.
3. Discuss heterosexual bias and identify the source of anti-gay prejudice, including religion and the military, and how to decrease it.
4. Compare and contrast the different forms of sexual aggression, including acquaintance, stranger, marital, and gang rape.
5. Explain the impact of rape on its survivors, including rape trauma syndrome.
6. Describe the means of preventing sexual assault.
7. Identify the preconditions and forms of child sexual abuse, including characteristics of children at risk.
8. Describe initial and long-term effects of sexual abuse and sexual abuse trauma.
9. Discuss the principles involved in child abuse prevention programs and obstacles to implementation.
10. Discuss the different meanings given to the Thomas/Hill hearings by whites and African Americans.

PRACTICE TEST QUESTIONS

Multiple Choice

1. Recent laws extending sexual harassment to include a hostile environment apply to:
   a. work situations at companies with more than 50 employees
   b. work situations at all businesses regardless of the number of employees
   c. only working women
   d. public institutions only

2. Sexual harassment is a mixture of sex and:
   a. flirting
   b. telling dirty jokes
   c. power
   d. violence

3. The factors that need to be examined to separate flirtation from sexual harassment include all of the following EXCEPT:
   a. whether you have equal power
   b. whether you are approached appropriately
   c. whether you wish to continue the contact
   d. whether you are the more attractive person

4. When college students were given a list of behaviors that might be seen as sexual harassment:
   a. men and women identified the same amount of behaviors as harassment
   b. women identified more of the behaviors as sexual harassment
   c. men identified more of the behaviors as sexual harassment
   d. neither identified the behaviors as harassment because force was not used

5. According to the Merit Systems Protection Board study of federal employees, sexual harassment:
   a. rarely occurred
   b. was almost always done by male supervisors to women employees
   c. was never done to male employees by female superiors
   d. occurred more frequently between co-workers

6. A broad term that refers to any kind of sexual activity initiated with another person through the use of argument, pressure, pleading, and cajoling, as well as force, pressure, alcohol or drugs, or authority is:
   a. sexual aggression
   b. sexual coercion
   c. acquaintance aggression
   d. acquaintance rape

7. Date rapes:
   a. are usually planned in advance
   b. often involve the use of alcohol or drugs
   c. seldom occur in fraternities, because others are around
   d. are easily recognized by both participants as date rape

8. Marital rape:
   a. is not recognized by any states because it is not "real" rape
   b. is a rare occurrence
   c. leaves the victim experiencing betrayal, anger, humiliation, and guilt
   d. is only recognized as a crime in Oregon

9. The most brutal rapes in which sex and aggression are violently fused are usually:
   a. sadistic rapes
   b. power rapes
   c. anger rapes
   d. date rapes

10. Most victims of rape:
    a. experience minor physical injuries as a result of the rape
    b. experience depression, anxiety, restlessness, or guilt as a result of the rape
    c. experience major physical injuries as a result of the rape
    d. report the incident to the police

11. Long-term effects of sexual abuse often include all the following EXCEPT:
    a. depression
    b. self-destructive tendencies, including suicide attempts and thoughts
    c. interpersonal relationship difficulties
    d. less vulnerability to rape or marital violence because of increased awareness

True/False

Mark T or F on the line before the question.

____ 1. Due to current laws, unwelcomed whistles, taunts, or looking over someone else's body is considered illegal in most states.

____ 2. Cultural and gender differences may contribute to confusion about what is sexual harassment.

____ 3. Incidents of sexual harassment do not usually occur to a victim until their late teenage years.

____ 4. The amount of gay violence has been exaggerated in the media, and is actually quite rare.

____ 5. Heterosexual women tend to be more tolerant of homosexuality than heterosexual men.

____ 6. Institutional sources of anti-gay prejudice include religion and the military.

____ 7. The typical stranger rape involves an assailant who attacks a stranger in a public place in the dark.

____ 8. Sexual assault against men may be perpetrated by other men or women.

____ 9. Almost all victims of child sexual abuse are females.

____ 10. The most traumatic form of sexual victimization is believed to be father-daughter abuse.

Fill-In

1. The use of power for sexual ends or the creation of a hostile environment of a sexual nature is known as

   ____________________ ____________________.

2. The tendency to see the world in heterosexual terms and to ignore or devalue homosexuality is known as

   ____________________ ____________________, or heterosexism.

3. ____________________ ____________________ is any kind of sexual activity against a person's will

   gained through the use of force, pressure, alcohol or drugs, or authority.

4. Sexual intercourse with a dating partner that occurs against his/her will and with force or the threat of force is

   known as ____________________ ____________________ or ____________________

   ____________________.

5. Consensual sex with a female under the legal age of consent is known as ____________________

____________________.

6. Victims of rape often experience ____________________ ____________________

____________________, which involves emotional changes an individual undergoes as a result of rape.

7. Any sexual interaction from fondling to genital penetration that occurs between an adult and a child is known as ____________________ ____________________ ____________________.

8. When the sexual abuse is between biologically-related individuals or step relatives, it is known as

____________________ ____________________.

9. Violence directed against gay men or lesbians because of their orientation is known as

____________________ ____________________.

10. Sexual intercourse between people too closely related to legally marry is defined as ________________.

acquaintance rape	intrafamilial abuse
child sexual abuse	rape trauma syndrome
date rape	sexual aggression
gay bashing	sexual harassment
heterosexual bias	statutory rape
incest	

Short Answer

1. Describe how the practices of some boys towards girls in early and middle childhood, such as "teasing," flipping up their skirts, or poking them with pencils, can contribute to an acceptance of sexual harassment in adulthood.

2. What are the three main sources of anti-gay prejudice in individuals, and what are two characteristics of these individuals?

3. How do sexual scripts and verbal and non-verbal communication affect interactions and thus lead to sexual coercion?

4. Describe the two phases of rape trauma syndrome and their effects on the victim's sexuality. What steps can be taken to help in recovery?

5. What three factors put children at risk for sexual abuse, and what are three of the initial effects of the abuse?

ANSWERS TO PRACTICE TEST QUESTIONS

Multiple Choice

1. b
2. c
3. d
4. b
5. d
6. b
7. b
8. c
9. a
10. b
11. d

True/False

1. F
2. T
3. F
4. F
5. T
6. T
7. F
8. T
9. F
10. T

Fill-In

1. sexual harassment
2. heterosexual bias
3. Sexual aggression
4. date rape, acquaintance rape
5. statutory rape
6. rape trauma syndrome
7. child sexual abuse
8. intrafamilial abuse
9. gay bashing
10. incest

Short Answer

1. Page 718
2. Page 725
3. Pages 732–733
4. Pages 741–742
5. Pages 750–751

OBSERVATIONS AND REFLECTIONS

OBSERVATION

Does It Happen at Your School? Part 1

Look in your school catalog or call someone in Student Services to find out what is the official policy for handling accusations of sexual harassment on your campus. Answer the following questions.

Is there an official policy?

What is that policy?

To whom is sexual harassment reported?

How is it followed up?

Would you file a report if you were sexually harassed?

Why or why not?

Inquire at the same office if there have been any reported incidents of sexual harassment? How many?

Have any been anti-gay/lesbian harassment?

If there were, how were they handled?

What was the outcome for each case?

What was the attitude of the person you spoke to about sexual harassment on college campuses?

OBSERVATION

Does It Happen at Your School? Part 2

College campuses are prime areas for date rape to happen, and a great deal of media attention has been devoted to this recently. Most campuses are paying more attention to this issue by having educational meetings at dorms, sororities, fraternities, and other groups. To find out the answers to some of the questions listed below you may need to contact Student Services, campus police, or the student health service.

Have there been any incidents of rape reported on your campus in the last three years?

Was the person caught?

Have there been any incidents of date rape on your campus reported in the last three years?

What was the outcome of the situation?

If there were any incidents, were they related to any specific groups such as athletes or fraternities?

If there were any incidents, was alcohol or drugs involved?

What services are available for people who have been victims of rape or harassment at school or other places? List both school and community resources.

Find a hot-line number that deals with this issue to keep, so if you or anyone you know needs help you will know who to call.

OBSERVATION

Preventing Childhood Sexual Abuse

The scandals involving childhood sexual abuse have received a great deal of attention. Since these episodes and the public awareness they generated, there have been more and more efforts made at prevention. In this activity you can see what type of education and materials on this subject are available in your community.

1. **Library** Find a book on prevention of sexual abuse written for children. An example of a book like this is *A Better Safe Than Sorry Book* by Sol and Judith Gordon. Read it or another similar book and answer these questions. These books are short and don't take long to read!

   If you were a parent would you read this to your child?

   Would it make any difference if your child was a boy or girl?

   What age would your child be when you introduced this concept?

   How do you think you would have felt if this book was read to you at that age?

   Do you think this book might scare children, or have any negative effects on their sexual feelings?

2. **Video Store** Many video stores have the video for children to watch called *Strong Kids, Safe Kids.* It is aimed at preventing child sexual abuse and is moderated by Henry Winkler. Watch this video and answer these questions.

   If you were a parent would you watch this video with your child?

   Would it make any difference if your child was a boy or girl?

   What age would you want your child to be when you watched this video?

   Do you think this video might scare children, or have any negative effects on their sexual feelings?

3. **Police Department** Call your local police department and see if they have any materials (some have "comic books") that they distribute for use with children. Read them and answer the same questions under the library section.

4. **Schools** Call your local school district and find out what types of education they provide about sexual abuse. If materials are available to view, review them and answer the same questions under the library section.

PERSONAL INVOLVEMENT ASSESSMENT

DATE RAPE

Date, or acquaintance, rape is an act of violence, aggression, and power. It is forced, manipulated, or coerced sexual intercourse with a friend or an acquaintance.

Acquaintance rape can happen anywhere, at any time, to anyone, but occurs more frequently among college students, particularly in their first year, than among any other age group. There is no single solution to preventing acquaintance rape; however, it can be helpful to be aware of its potential for occurring.

Two Stories

Ann: "I met him at a party. He was really good looking and he had a great smile. I wanted to meet him but I wasn't sure how. I didn't want to appear too forward. Then he came over and introduced himself. We talked and found we had a lot in common. I really liked him. When he asked me over to his place for a drink, I thought it would be OK. He was such a good listener, and I wanted him to ask me out again.

"When we got to his room the only place to sit was on the bed. I didn't want him to get the wrong idea but what else could I do? We talked for a while and then he made his move. I was so startled. He started by kissing. I really liked him so the kissing was nice. But then he pushed me down on the bed. I tried to get up and I told him to stop. He was so much bigger and stronger. I got scared and I started to cry. I froze and he raped me.

"It took only a couple of minutes and it was terrible, he was so rough. When it was over he kept asking me what was wrong like he didn't know. He had just forced himself on me and said he wanted to see me again. I'm so afraid to see him. I never thought it would happen to me."

Jim: "I first met her at a party. She looked real hot, wearing a sexy dress that showed off her great body. We started talking right away. I knew that she liked me by the way she kept smiling and touching my arm while she was speaking. She seemed pretty relaxed so I asked her back to my place for a drink... When she said 'yes,' I knew that I was going to be lucky!

"When we got to my place we sat on the bed kissing. At first, everything was great. Then, when I started to lay her down on the bed, she started twisting and saying she didn't want to. Most girls don't like to appear too easy so I knew she was just going through the motions. When she stopped struggling I knew that she would have to throw in some tears before we did it.

"She was still very upset afterwards and I just don't understand it! If she didn't want to have sex why did she come back to my room with me? You could tell by the way she dressed and acted that she was no virgin, so why she had to put up such a big struggle I don't know."

What happened? He thought she wanted to have sex with him and that she didn't really mean it when she said "No!" She didn't want to have sex, but was afraid to be more assertive in telling him. This was an example of *acquaintance rape.*

What do you think about this situation? Write down your responses to the following questions about the situation.

Who was in the wrong?

Source: A brochure, *Acquaintance Rape: Is Dating Dangerous?* prepared by ACHA (American College Health Association), Baltimore, MD, 1987.

Who had the responsibility to stop what was happening?

Should Ann have gone to Jim's room? Why or why not?

Should Jim have assumed that Ann wanted to have sex based on her dress and her willingness to go to his apartment? Why or why not?

Should Jim have assumed that Ann was not a virgin based on her dress? Why or why not?

What do you think Ann should have done differently?

What do you think Jim should have done differently?

REFLECTION

The Line Between Harassment and Flirtation

Drawing the line between flirtation and harassment is not always easy and can be filled with ambiguity. Read over the following stories, and note whether you believe someone is being harassed.

1. Jack and Hillary work together at a law office. Jack tells Hillary she looks really great in her new dress, and later asks her out to dinner. She says no. He asks her out again the next week.

   Is this harassment?

   What should Hillary do?

   What would you do if you were Hillary?

2. Mike and Susan work together. Mike is constantly telling sexually explicit jokes to the other workers while Susan is around. He also keeps making compliments about Susan's figure. The last few days he has started to playfully pat her rear end, and tell her how cute it looks.

   Is this harassment?

   What should Susan do?

   What would you do if you were Susan?

Ask a friend or classmate of the other sex to do this same exercise and compare your answers.

What parts of your answers are the same?

What differences were there?

GENDER AND SEXUAL IDENTITY QUESTIONS

One of the aspects this chapter deals with are the negative sexual experiences people can have. Sometimes it can be difficult to recognize and acknowledge that something that has happened was sexual abuse. Sometimes people try to deny these experiences, or they recall memories that are uncomfortable but they don't label it as sexual abuse. The problem with not acknowledging these experiences is that they can affect our sexuality in other ways. Dealing with the experience and the feelings we have from it can change us from a victim to a survivor and make our futures more positive. As the textbook points out, sexual abuse happens to both men and women. Answer the following questions that apply to you.

- When I was a child something that happened to me that I now recognize as sexual abuse was . . . .
  - At the time it happened the way I felt about it was . . . .
  - Now when I think about it I feel . . . .
- I have been affected by sexual harassment when . . . .
  - At the time I realized/didn't realize it was harassment and so . . . .
- I think that I have/have not been tricked into having sex (when . . .)
  - At the time it happened I felt . . . .
  - When I think about it now I feel . . . .

- I have/have not been forced into having sex when . . . .

    - At the time it happened I felt . . . .

    - When I think about it now I feel . . . .

- My attitude toward gay and lesbian people is . . . .

    - When I think about why I feel that way I think it is because . . . .

The first time I can remember anything about the abuse, I must have been about five years old. The perpetrator was a member of my own family—an uncle by marriage. I seem to remember this man fondling me in front of his own children. Having no recollection of the abuse, I tried things with boys and girls never knowing why. I always felt disgusted and ashamed of my behavior and didn't tell a soul. I also had other cousins, both females and males, try things with me. I don't blame these particular individuals since they too were molested by the same individual. I now know as an adult that children (humans) learn through experience, and one can't reenact a situation that they have never experienced. —27-year-old female Hispanic

As I got closer to the bed, (an acquaintance) Tom pushed me down. I was on my stomach lying on the bed while he was sitting on my back. I asked him, "What are you doing?" Still, I didn't feel any threat from him. Tom started to touch my body and said, "I want to f___ you." "What?" I replied. "Let me f___ you", he said. "No! I don't like doing that." He pulled my underwear down and began squeezing my butt. "Don't do that," I said. Then, he jammed his fingers into my anus. Boy, was it uncomfortable. I gave him a quick jolt and pushed him off me. I ran to the bathroom and locked the door. I was scared. Tom pounded on the door, pleading, "Let me in, let me touch you, I come very quick." When I look back at the incident, I felt like I was exploited of my rights, my privacy, and my security. —24-year-old male Vietnamese

This very good friend of mine, I thought, walked me back to my dorm room. Shortly afterwards, he began holding me and kissing me in a romantic way. I went along with it because I was vulnerable, and I felt that he cared a great deal for me. Unfortunately, he began fondling me and slowly started removing my clothes. As he got down to my panties I realized that this was wrong, and I didn't want or like him in that way; so the terror began.

I was so afraid and unsure of what was going to happen so I said, "I don't want to do anything." Soon he began to get very angry, holding me down firmly and sucking my breasts. As he moved toward my crotch, I started crying and begged him to stop. He was so upset he started choking me and said, "You shouldn't let a guy take you that far because the next time it won't be this easy." I felt so embarrassed and humiliated. I was terrified of this person but never told anyone what had happened because I felt it was all my fault. —23-year-old Black female

CHAPTER 19
COMMERCIAL SEX

CHAPTER OUTLINE

Sexually Oriented Material in Contemporary America
- Is It Pornography or Erotica?
- *Perspective 1: Changing Perspectives on Obscenity*
- Sexually Oriented Material and Popular Culture
- Technology and Sexually Oriented Material
- The Effects of Sexually Oriented Material
- Censorship, Sexually Oriented Material, and the Law
- *Perspective 2: Rock, Rap, and Righteousness: Censorship and Popular Music*

Prostitution
- Females Working in Prostitution
- Males Working in Prostitution
- Prostitution and the Law

LEARNING OBJECTIVES

At the conclusion of Chapter 19, students should be able to:

1. Distinguish the differences in meanings between sexually oriented material, pornography, and erotica.
2. Discuss changing perspectives as to what constitutes pornography, including the role of deviance and moral outrage and the significance of personal response.
3. Describe the impact of technology in the dissemination of sexually oriented material through computers, the telephone, and VCRs, including how videocassettes have changed the viewing audience.
4. Discuss the reasons people use sexually oriented material.
5. Evaluate arguments concerning the impact of sexually oriented material on behavior, especially aggression against women and gender discrimination.
6. Discuss child pornography, including its impact on children, laws against it, and debate about its extent.
7. Evaluate the arguments concerning the censorship of sexually oriented material, including legal issues revolving around obscenity, as well as popular music.
8. Discuss female prostitution, including subculture, motivation, and types of prostitution.
9. Discuss male prostitution, including differences between delinquent and gay male prostitutes.
10. Discuss prostitution and the law, including decriminalization, regulation, and the HIV/AIDS epidemic.

PRACTICE TEST QUESTIONS

Multiple Choice

1. Sexually explicit material that depicts intimate sexual activities and/or the genitals is called:
   a. hardcore
   b. softcore
   c. erotica
   d. pornography
2. The Miss America Pageant and *Penthouse* magazine:
   a. illustrate some of the problems in labeling material as obscene
   b. provide a clear definition between what is obscene and what is not
   c. are both socially acceptable ways of defining beauty and attractiveness
   d. portray a clear boundary between what is legitimate and what is illegitimate
3. Anonymous telephone sex provides the caller with:
   a. a sense of reality about the needs and desires of others
   b. pseudo-intimacy and a sense of physical closeness
   c. inexpensive yet honest feedback about sexuality
   d. support and referral for sexual needs and desires
4. People who read or view sexually explicit material:
   a. usually recognize it as fantasy
   b. use it as a release from their everyday world
   c. find that it may activate a person's typical behavioral pattern
   d. all of the above may occur
5. Child pornography, a form of child sexual exploitation:
   a. occurs to children usually between the ages of 12 to 19
   b. involves children who are aware that their photographs are being used sexually
   c. most often involves children who are unrelated to the photographer
   d. involves children who are motivated by friendship, interest in sexuality, offers of money or threats
6. Prostitutes:
   a. are more likely to be accepted by their conventional peers who often admire their chosen profession
   b. separate sex as a physical act for which they are paid from sex as an expression of intimacy and pleasure
   c. are as likely as anyone else to have been sexually abused as children
   d. have been shown to have a relatively high self-concept
7. Of the following, who is the most likely to have a pimp?
   a. adolescent girls and streetwalkers
   b. call girls and masseuses
   c. older prostitutes
   d. male prostitutes
8. When women describe the most attractive things about their lives in the prostitution subculture, they describe:
   a. the excitement of their lives
   b. the attraction and intimacy they have with their pimp
   c. the monetary and material rewards
   d. the sexual fulfillment they feel
9. The most numerous prostitutes are those who are:
   a. call girls
   b. masseurs
   c. those who work in brothels
   d. streetwalkers

10. The only sexual offense for which women are extensively prosecuted is:
    a. exhibitionism
    b. sexual addiction
    c. prostitution
    d. fellatio

True/False

Mark T or F on the line before the question.

____ 1. Studies indicate that the majority of people support the right of adults to possess sexually explicit materials.

____ 2. Clear definitions exist between what is obscene and what is not.

____ 3. There is no evidence to indicate that nonviolent sexually oriented material is associated with actual sexual aggression against women.

____ 4. While the courts have continually opposed censoring sexually explicit material, a major exception is child pornography.

____ 5. Child pornography has a vast and widespread audience.

____ 6. In recent years the printed word has become legally protected as an established art form and means of expression.

____ 7. Many women who accept money or drugs for sexual activities do not consider themselves to be prostitutes.

____ 8. The laws to end and/or control prostitution have been quite effective in ending it.

____ 9. Prostitutes do not appear to be at any higher risk for contracting HIV/AIDS than the general sexually active population.

____ 10. In contrast to male delinquent prostitutes, gay male prostitutes engage in prostitution as a means of expressing their sexuality *and* making money.

Fill-In

1. The term derived from the Greek meaning a love poem and which describes a positive evaluation of sexually oriented material is ____________________.

2. The term which represents a negative evaluation of sexually oriented material is ____________________.

3. Material such as photographs, videos, films, magazines, or books whose primary themes, topics, or depictions involve sexuality or cause sexual arousal are called ____________________ ____________________ material.

4. Material that intimately depicts sexual activities or genitals are called ____________________ ____________________ material.

5. With the invention of photography and the ability to reprint photographs, TV cable programs and computer-directed "virtual reality," ____________________ has transformed the production of sexually oriented material.

6. Erotic films catering to women or couples and which tend to avoid violence, are less male-centered, and are more sensitive to women's erotic fantasies are termed ____________________ ____________________.

7. When the government, private groups, or individuals impose their moral or political values on others by suppressing works, ideas, or images they deem offensive, it is called ____________________.

8. Though difficult to arrive at a legal definition, ____________________ is the state of being contrary to generally accepted moral standards.

9. Prostitution forms its own ____________________ by having its own hierarchy, code of conduct, and vocabulary.

10. The ____________________ ____________________ subculture, an antisocial youth culture, is part of a delinquent street life characterized by male and female drug dealing and theft.

censorship	pornography
erotica	sexually explicit
femme porn	sexually oriented
obscenity	subculture
peer delinquent	technology

Essay

1. List and briefly describe two ways that technology has transformed and extended the ways in which sexually oriented material is conveyed.

2. Describe three functions of sexually oriented material.

3. Briefly identify and discuss two opposing viewpoints regarding the impact of sexually explicit material on women.

4. List and describe two problems that make it difficult to arrive at a legal definition of obscenity.

5. Describe several motivations for women who become prostitutes.

ANSWERS TO PRACTICE TEST QUESTIONS

Multiple Choice

1. a
2. a
3. b
4. d
5. d
6. b
7. a
8. c
9. d
10. c

True/False

1. T
2. F
3. T
4. T
5. F
6. T
7. T
8. F
9. F
10. T

Fill-In

1. erotica
2. pornography
3. sexually oriented
4. sexually explicit
5. technology
6. femme porn
7. censorship
8. obscenity
9. subculture
10. peer delinquent

Essay

1. Pages 764–766
2. Page 767
3. Pages 767–769
4. Pages 776–777
5. Pages 780–781

OBSERVATIONS AND REFLECTIONS

OBSERVATION

Pornography or Obscenity—You Be the Judge

If you are not comfortable viewing erotica, then choose something you are comfortable with evaluating, i.e., *Cosmopolitan,* a romance novel, or beauty contest.

Choose a medium such as movies (available in home video), photographs, magazines, printed word, computer (e-mail), "virtual reality," or another source which sells or promotes sexually explicit materials. For a moment, become "clinical" when you review the material. As you respond to the questions below, keep in mind the following definitions:

pornography:	Sexually oriented material that is negatively evaluated
obscenity:	That which is deemed offensive to "accepted" standards of decency or morality
softcore:	Non-explicit sexually oriented material
hardcore:	Sexually explicit material that intimately depicts sexual activities or the genitals

Fill in the following:

Name of medium

Theme of medium

Audience for which it is intended

What messages were sent?

How were these messages conveyed?

Was violence utilized?

If so, to whom was it directed?

How would you label this material? (see definitions above)

Potential effect it might have on its audience

REFLECTION

Ruling On the Legality of Sex for Profit

For a moment, consider yourself a member of the United States Supreme Court. Given the definitions and discussion provided about sexually explicit material, think for a moment how you might vote on the following issues:

1. a minor (17-year-old male) posing nude for photographs to be displayed and distributed in a national magazine
2. a prostitute (24-year-old female) soliciting for business in her own surroundings (brothel or apartment)
3. a prostitute (24-year-old male) soliciting for business on a public sidewalk and using local hotels, cars, and/or back alleys to conduct his business
4. providing funding for prostitutes in order that they can, regularly and without cost to them, be checked for HIV and other STDs
5. sexually explicit photographs/artwork exhibited in a metropolitan public art gallery

What criteria did you use to evaluate each of the above? If you stated "subjective" or provided opinions based on your personal biases and experiences, then you are very much like those who indeed judge and legislate.

If you had to classify your views as liberal, neutral, or conservative, how would you articulate yours? What do you feel influenced your attitude about sexually explicit materials?

GENDER AND SEXUAL IDENTITY QUESTIONS

If your experiences involve the use of erotica and you feel that it has had a significant impact on your sex education, sexual fantasies, and/or sexual practices, then you may wish to complete the following questions and include this section as a component of your gender and sexual identity paper.

- The first time I saw pornography was when . . . .

- My reaction was . . . .

- The primary medium I utilized to sexually stimulate or help to eroticize my sex life was . . . .

- I used sexually explicit material when I felt . . . .

- It helped to make me feel . . . .

- From the materials, I learned . . . .

- The most negative impact it has had on me is . . . .

- The most positive impact it has had on me is . . . .

- In terms of its influence on my relationships with others, I feel that erotica . . . .

My parents did not mind me looking at my father's Playboy. *In fact, at 16 they gave me my own subscription!* —24-year-old male Caucasian reminisced about his exposure to pornography

She (my aunt) actually started molesting me when I was six. She would come home late at night, drunk, and carry me into her bed so that she could perform oral sex on me. She molested me until I was 12 years old. She was a prostitute so later in my molestation she tried to include her tricks, but I cried my way out of it every time. —26-year-old African Mexican Native American female

(My friend) Richard's parents thought cartoons were too violent. His family answered the door naked, they were always naked if they were at home. I would watch pornographic movies on Select TV (movie channel) late at night. My friends and I would discuss sex all the time, yet most of our assumptions were wrong. I turned to pornography and friends to learn about sex as opposed to the institutions that were supposed to teach it. —25-year-old male Caucasian

VALUES SURVEY REVIEW

Long, long ago, (at the beginning of the semester!) you were asked to complete a values survey. (See the Personal Involvement Assessment in Chapter 2 of this book.) Without looking back at your responses, again answer these questions.

SA	CIRCLE IF YOU STRONGLY AGREE	FEMALE _____
A	CIRCLE IF YOU MODERATELY AGREE	MALE _______
N	CIRCLE IF YOU HAVE NO OPINION	
D	CIRCLE IF YOU MODERATELY DISAGREE	
SD	CIRCLE IF YOU STRONGLY DISAGREE	

STATEMENT		LEVEL OF AGREEMENT
A.	You should only have sex with someone you love.	SA A N D SD
B.	Masturbation is a healthy, acceptable form of sexual behavior.	SA A N D SD
C.	A woman should feel able to be as sexually assertive as a man.	SA A N D SD
D.	Abortions should be available to any woman who desires to terminate a pregnancy.	SA A N D SD
E.	Transvestites are psychologically dysfunctional.	SA A N D SD
F.	Prostitution should be a crime.	SA A N D SD
G.	Magazines like *Penthouse* and *Playboy* should be available at liquor stores.	SA A N D SD
H.	Homosexuality is unnatural and immoral.	SA A N D SD
I.	High school clinics should provide birth control.	SA A N D SD
J.	All doctors should be tested for HIV, and patients notified of status.	SA A N D SD
K.	Parents should be notified and give permission before their daughters can have an abortion.	SA A N D SD
L.	All hospital patients should be tested for HIV, and doctors notified of status.	SA A N D SD
M.	If a 15-year-old boy has consensual sex with a 20-year-old female, she should be arrested.	SA A N D SD
N.	If a 15-year-old girl has consensual sex with a 20-year-old male, he should be arrested.	SA A N D SD
O.	Surrogate motherhood should be legal.	SA A N D SD
P.	Rape is often charged because women regret what they did.	SA A N D SD
Q.	A boy who has not had sex by the time he is 17 is weird.	SA A N D SD

Compare the results from the beginning of the semester to now. How are they similar or different?

What do you feel influenced these changes?

How might your survey have appeared if you had taken it two years ago?

In what direction do you feel your values are moving?

How do you think your parents might answer these questions?

What about your best friend and/or a partner?

If you would like, ask a trusted person to complete the survey and discuss responses with him or her.

A FINAL MESSAGE TO STUDENTS

Tell Us What You Think

The authors of this study guide hope that it has been beneficial to you. The best way we can improve it is by your feedback. We would like to hear from you. You can fill out this form and mail it to us (you can take this page out and fold it so the address on the other side is showing). You can also contact us on EMAIL through Internet at bobbim @ beach1.csulb.edu.

Male ______ Female ______ Age _____ Date ________________

School

Instructor

1. What parts of the study guide did you use?

	ALWAYS	USUALLY	SOMETIMES	1-2	NEVER
A. Chapter Outline					
B. Learning Objectives					
C. Multiple Choice					
D. True-False/Matching					
E. Key Terms Fill-Ins					
F. Short Answer Questions					
G. Essay Questions					
H. Observations					
I. Reflections					
J. Gender and Sexual Identity Sections					

2. What parts of the study guide were most helpful?

3. What parts of the study guide were least helpful?

4. What other assessments or things would you like to see included in this study guide?

5. Did your instructor have you do any of the observations or reflections for the class? If yes, which one(s)?

6. Did you share the personal exercise in the book with others (partner, parents, friends, etc.)?

7. If yes to Question 6, what was their reaction, and what was the result?

8. Did you do the sexual identity assignment for your own information or for a class assignment?

9. What other comments do you have about the book? (You can write on the back where indicated—then fold and send.)

Additional Comments

Place

stamp

here

To: Mayfield Publishing Company
1280 Villa Street
Mountain View, CA 94041

Mitzenmacher/Sayad Study Guide

Fold this part last.

NOTES

NOTES

NOTES

NOTES

NOTES

NOTES

NOTES

NOTES

NOTES

NOTES